Small Farms
Are Real
Farms

Sustaining People through Agriculture

Small Farms Are Real Farms

Sustaining People through Agriculture

John Ikerd

Acres U.S.A.
Austin, Texas

Small Farms Are Real Farms

Copyright © 2008 John Ikerd

Acres U.S.A.
P.O. Box 91299
Austin, Texas 78709 U.S.A.
(512) 892-4400 • fax (512) 892-4448
info@acresusa.com • www.acresusa.com

Printed in the United States of America

Publisher's Cataloging-in-Publication

Ikerd, John, 1939-
Small farms are real farms / John Ikerd. Austin, TX, ACRES U.S.A., 2008
xviii, 254 pp., 23 cm.
Includes Index
Includes Bibliography
ISBN 978-1-60173-006-0 (trade)

1. United States Rural conditions. 2. United States Social conditions
3. Sustainable agriculture United States. 4. Farm management.
5. Sociology, rural United States. 6. Farms, Small United States.
I. Ikerd, John, 1939- II. Small farms are real farms: Sustaining people through agriculture.

S441   630

■| Contents

SUSTAINING AGRICULTURE

MANAGEMENT

ECONOMICS

MARKETS

Also by John Ikerd

Sustainable Capitalism

A Return to Common Sense

Crisis and Opportunity:
Sustainability in American Agriculture

Preface

mall farms are real farms. Our occupations, paid or unpaid, are important reflections of who we are. Most people who live and work on small farms clearly identify themselves as farmers. In recent years, many operators of larger farming operations have taken to calling themselves growers, feeders, contract producers, or agri-businesspeople, which more clearly identifies the specific nature of their enterprises. But most small farmers still call themselves farmers.

The significance of a farm is commonly defined by its total amount of production, its size of operation, or the total amount of income it generates. Since small farmers typically produce less, own less, and earn less than large farmers, small farmers are not considered to be real farmers, even though small farms outnumber large farms by ten to one. If people on small farms have a problem, it's treated as a social problem, rather than a farm problem. Successful small farms are written off as aberrations rather than meaningful examples for other farmers. Small farms are simply not considered to be real farms.

The logical and factual consequences of such thinking are examined in this book — the degradation of health and natural productivity of the land, the economic and social decay of rural communities, the diminishing quality of life of farm families, and the growing risks to national food security. The fundamental purpose of farming is to enhance the quality of life of people — farmers, rural residents, consumers, and society in general. In this regard, the industrialization of agriculture, which inevitably has led to fewer and larger farms, has failed miserably.

In the fall of 1999, I was given an opportunity to give a plenary address at the USDA National Small Farm Conference held in St. Louis, Missouri. The first chapter of this book, "A Small Farm Revolution," is the paper I wrote for that presentation. It is a call for the rejection of industrial agriculture and a return to smaller, more diversified family farms as the only logical means of restoring sustainability to American agriculture. The articles which make up the rest of this book were written for *Small Farm Today* magazine, with few exceptions between 2000 and 2007. I wrote these articles because I wanted to share the new vision of sustainable agriculture with families on small farms all across the nation. Some of the core ideas were repeated in different articles so that each article could be understood on its own. Together, the articles paint a picture of the challenges and opportunities confronting those who live and work on small farms.

While sustainable farming may not be impossible on a big farm, or inevitable on a small farm, sustainable farms are far more likely to be smaller rather than larger. Industrial agriculture has encouraged *extensive* management — more acres, more dollars per farmer — and thus bigger farms. Sustainable farming requires *intensive* management — more farmers per acre, per dollar — and thus smaller farms. Sustainable farming does not mean returning to the small, diversified family farms of the past, but it does mean moving into the future with farms far smaller than those dominating American agriculture today.

Sustainable farming is about stewardship, but it is not about sacrificing the present for the future. It is about the pursuit of happiness today. Happiness is not simply a matter of economic or material self-interest; it is also about family, neighbors, and a sense of belonging; about stewardship, citizenship, and a sense of purpose and meaning. Sustainable farming would be far easier if government farm policies rewarded citizenship and stewardship, rather than exploitation and extraction. Such policies would lead to smaller farms and more farmers.

Americans are increasingly concerned about their food choices and many are showing a strong preference for foods that are produced both sustainably and locally, by farmers that they know and trust. They want food that is safe, healthful, and nutritious, but also food that is produced by methods that respect the natural environment, the land, and the people who produce, process, and distribute it. They are willing to pay the full cost of food produced with ecological and social integrity. The new food culture is creating new opportunities for small farms.

The only true source of national food security is in the natural productivity of a nation's land, and the willingness and ability of its farmers to maintain the productivity of its land for the benefit of its people. The corporations that increasingly control American agriculture are not people and thus have no families, no communities, and no citizenship. National food security depends on having *real* people in control of our food system and *real* farmers on our farms.

Sustainable small farmers of the future must be willing and able to "think outside of the industrial boxes" of specialization, standardization, and consolidation. They must reject the new technologies of industrialization and learn to manage and nurture their farms as complex, interconnected living systems. To meet the challenges and opportunities of farming in the future, farmers must reject the conventional wisdom of agricultural industrialization and embrace the common sense of agricultural sustainability. Farmers of the future must be thinking workers and working thinkers, as well as thoughtful, caring people. They must be real farmers. That's what this book is about.

■| Acknowledgments

I first want to express my appreciation to Ron Macher, the longtime editor of *Small Farm Today* magazine. Ron has been gracious enough to continue to publish my articles over the years, with no restraint on either the topics I chose to address or the tone in which I chose to address them. Some of the topics may seem a bit "far out" and others may seem a "bit radical," but Ron has never questioned my judgment in writing about what I thought was of importance to those who live and work on small farms. I want to thank Ron also for encouraging me to publish the complete collection as a book.

I also want to thank Fred Walters, *Acres U.S.A.* publisher, for his willingness to take on this project and for guiding me through the process. I became aware of *Acres U.S.A.* soon after I became interested in sustainable agriculture in the early 1990s. I have gained a great deal of respect over the years for their work in promoting a sustainable, eco-agriculture for all types and sizes of farms. I am proud to have my name and work now affiliated with this organization.

Perhaps most important, I want to thank the people on small farms all across the nation from whom I have learned much of what I have written in this book. I have always thought that it would be easier to farm sustainably on a small farm. That's one of the reasons that I returned to the University of Missouri to finish my academic career. Missouri has a lot of small farms. I worked closely with Dyremple Marsh of the Small Farm Family Program at Lincoln University during the '90s and learned a lot from working with Dyremple, the small farms agents, and the farmers associated with this program. My work with small farmers in Missouri led to invitations to speak at small farm conferences all across the country, giving me an opportunity to take what I learned from farmers at one conference to teach at the next.

I also want to express my appreciation to my wife, Ellen. She diligently continues to read virtually everything I write, not only helping with the seemingly impossible process of proofing, but also finding passages that don't read as well as they should and offering valuable suggestions. But most important, she encourages me to continue to pursue my purpose and passion in life, which is to think and to share my thoughts concerning what needs to be done to create a more sustainable agriculture and a more sustainable economy and society. Without her support and encouragement I might continue to think, but I probably would not continue to write.

I also want to thank my extended family. I grew up on small dairy farm in southwest Missouri, and my younger brother still lives and works on that farm today — and it is still small. I learned about farm life first hand from my parents, who are now deceased, and my brothers and sisters. They helped me learn the most basic lessons of life, which is still an important reason that people chose to live on small family farms. Like a lot of others, I left the farm for college and never went back. It was a decision that made sense at the time. But I often tell young people today if I were 25 or 30 years old today, I would choose the life of a farmer. There are opportunities today for a good life on a small farm that simply did not exist 40 years ago. I firmly believe small farms will be the real farms of the future.

Foreword

I first want to express my appreciation to my long-time friend John Ikerd—a champion of the sustainable small farmer and rural communities. As a small farmer and publisher of *Small Farm Today* magazine, I also want to thank John for his kind words about all he has learned from small farmers across the nation.

It will be obvious after reading this book that John is an excellent writer. More importantly, he is a thinking writer who had the courage to change his viewpoint 180 degrees over the years.

I started as a farmer and John as a Professor of Agricultural Economics. We both accepted the standard agriculture lessons of the time: Bigger is Better, New is Always Better, and Specialization and Monoculture are Good Things. It took years of experiencing and listening to farmers — and the Rural Crisis in the 1970s and 1980s—for us to learn different. We have learned different and now John shares the real lessons of agriculture with you.

I applaud John for his praise concerning his wife in the Acknowledgments. Marriage is an important part of small farming — a good team effort is needed. It takes a physical, mental, and financial effort to get things accomplished on a sustainable farm.

After witnessing John's standing-ovation speeches in several arenas, it is clear how he binds to the sustainable small farm and its philosophies and ideals. He gives young people the greatest gift in life: hope for the future. He seals that commitment with the statement, "If I were 25-30 years old,

I would choose to be a small farmer, because I believe small farms will be the real farms of the future." I support and agree with him 100%.

Now you have a great book to read — and a lot of thinking to do. Enjoy it.

Ron Macher
Farmer and publisher of
Small Farm Today magazine
September 2007

THE
REVOLUTION

01 | A Small Farm Revolution

*A*merican agriculture is in crisis. Until recently, the crisis had been a quiet one. No one wanted to talk about it. Thousands of farm families were being forced off the land, but we were being told by the agricultural establishment that their exodus was inevitable, in fact, was a sign of progress. Those who failed were simply the victims of their own inefficiency — their inability to keep up with changing times, their inability to compete. But in fact, it's not inefficiency or resistance to change that is forcing families to leave their farms. It's our collective obsession with our short-run, self-interest. It's our worship of markets as the only true arbitrators of value. It's our acceptance of corporate greed as the only road to true prosperity. This crisis was neither inevitable nor was it a sign of progress. The people of America need to know the truth. The time for quietness has passed.

With farm prices at record low levels for two years running, the *agriculture establishment* has finally begun to take notice. Congress has passed emergency farm legislation. But even now, the farm crisis is being blamed on such mundane things as "exceptionally good" global weather, problems in Pacific Rim financial markets, European trade restrictions, and an inadequate government "safety net." The crisis is a simple matter of supply and demand, the economists say. The only solutions proposed by the so-called experts are to tinker with government policy or, better yet, to simply wait for markets to recover. The only alternatives farmers are being offered are to get big enough to be competitive, get a corporate contract to reduce risks, or get out of farming. But, getting big, giving in, or getting out are not the only alternatives. There are better alternatives for farmers and for society. The people need to be told the truth. The time for quietness has passed.

Crisis in agriculture is a chronic symptom of the type of agriculture we have been promoting in this country for the past fifty years. Reoccurring financial crises are the means by which we allow farms to become larger and more specialized so consumers can have more cheap food, and the means by which we free people from the "drudgery of farming" to find better occupations elsewhere. Or from another perspective, reoccurring crisis is the means by which we force farmers off the land.

The promise of profits lures farmers to buy into new cost cutting and production enhancing technologies. However, the resulting increases in production cause prices to fall, which eliminates previous profits for the innovators and drives the *laggards* out of business. This technology treadmill has been driving farmers off the land for decades. But the current crisis has an added dimension. The current crisis reflects a brazen attempt by the giant corporations to take control of agriculture away from family farms, to move beyond specialization and standardization, to centralize command and control — to complete the industrialization of agriculture. This final stage of industrialization is not only destroying the lives of farm families, it's polluting the natural environment, depleting the fertility of the land, and destroying rural communities. The industrialization of agriculture is not good for America. The people need to be told the truth. The time for quietness has passed.

As I recall, the creed of the Future Farmers of America begins with the words, "I believe in the future of farming with a faith born not of words but of deeds." For years I believed that creed and have spent much of my life trying to live by that creed, but I simply can no longer believe it is true. There is no future of farming, at least not farming as we have known it, not if the current industrialization of agriculture continues. Every time the average farm size goes up, the number of surviving farmers goes down. Every time a farmer signs a corporate production contract, an independent farmer becomes a "corporate hired hand." With every corporate merger in the global food system, the future of farming in America grows more dim.

The food and fiber industry most certainly has a future. People will always need food, clothing, and shelter, and someone will provide them. But there will be no future for farming, not true farming, not unless we have the courage to challenge and disprove the conventional wisdom that farmers must get bigger, give in to corporate control, or get out. There are better alternatives for farmers and for society. We must find the courage to challenge the conventional wisdom. People need to be told the truth about the future of farming. It's time for a revolution in American agriculture. The time for quietness has passed.

What's happening in agriculture today is no different from what has already happened in most other sectors of the economy, at least not different in concept. We are told that industrialization is the inevitable consequence of human enlightenment and technological progress. But the industrialization of agriculture is neither enlightened nor progressive. It is being driven by the same force that now threatens the integrity of our democratic society and the health of our natural environment — a blind faith in the economics of narrow, short-run self-interest. Industrialists have a deeply held faith that the promise of more profits, no matter how small, is the best means of allocating resources — whether it is allocation of people among alternative occupations, land among alternative uses, money among investments, or people among communities. All things that are possible and profitable are done in the name of economic progress.

However, the science of economics was never meant to be limited to the pursuit of the narrow, short-run self-interest of individuals. Adam Smith proclaimed more than 200 years ago, in his classic book, *The Wealth of Nations*, that each person pursuing their individual self-interest, results in the greatest good for society as a whole, as if guided by an "invisible hand." Smith's words revolutionized economic thinking and remain the foundation for conventional economic thought. But Smith certainly did not claim that only the narrow, self-interests of individuals were important. Instead, he simply observed that the broad interest of society in general seemed to be well served in the process of individuals pursuing their own short-run self-interest. Pursuit of self-interest seemed but a convenient means to a far nobler end.

Smith's invisible hand probably worked reasonably well 200 years ago, given the economy and society of that time. Most economic enterprises were small, family operations. For such operations, land, labor, capital, and management often resided in the same entity — typically, the family. Farming was still the dominant occupation. Few enterprises were large enough to have any impact on the marketplace as a whole. It was fairly easy for people to take on a new enterprise that seemed profitable and to drop one that seemed destined to lose money. Thus, profits were competed away and losses didn't persist in highly competitive local markets. In general, communications between individual producers and consumers were clear because their market connections were simple and often personal. All of these things were essential in the transformation of pursuit of self-interest into societal good.

In Smith's times, human populations also were small enough and technologies were sufficiently benign, so that actions of people had little permanent impact on the natural environment, at least on the global environment. Back then, strong cultural, moral, and social values dictated the norms and standards of acceptable individual behavior. Smith could not conceive of a society in which the welfare of the poor and hungry would not matter, or where people in general would behave in unethical or immoral ways. "No society can surely be flourishing and happy, in which the far greater part of the members are poor and miserable," he wrote.

In the environment of 200 years ago, when conventional economics was born, pursuit of self-interest might have served the interests of society reasonably well. But the world has changed over the past two centuries. Today, most sectors of the U.S. economy are dominated by large corporate enterprises. Corporations are inherently non-human entities — regardless of what the Supreme Court has said and regardless of the humanness of corporate managers and stockholders. The resources of land, labor, capital, and management are now separate entities, sometimes divided even among nations. And corporate profits are far larger than any concept of "normal" profit envisioned in classical economics. Producers and consumers have become disconnected, geographically and conceptually, as a consequence of industrialization. Consumers no longer have personal knowledge of where their products come from or of who is involved in their production. They must rely on a complex set of standards, rules, and regulations for product information, and today's advertising consists of *disinformation,* by design.

In today's society, there are no logical reasons to believe that pursuit of self-interest is the best means of meeting the needs of society. But powerful economic and political interests have tremendous stakes in maintaining the belief in an *invisible hand.* It justifies their selfishness and greed. It legitimizes their endless accumulation of economic wealth. Thoughtful economists know the assumptions which must hold for truly competitive markets are no longer valid. But few have the courage to speak out. The economic assumptions of 200 years ago are no longer adequate. It's time to rethink the economic foundation for our society. We need to face the truth.

In addition, human activities are no longer ecologically benign if they ever really were. The pressures of growing populations and rising per capita consumption are now depleting resources of the land far faster than they can be regenerated by nature. Wastes and contaminants from human activities are being generated at rates far in excess of the capacity of the natural environment to absorb and detoxify them. Fossil fuels, the engine of twentieth-century economic development, are being depleted at rates infinitely faster than they can ever be replenished. Human population pressures are destroying other biological species, upon which the survival of humanity ultimately depends. The human species is now capable of destroying almost everything that makes up the biosphere we call Earth, including humanity itself. The economics of Adam Smith didn't address environmental issues, and neither do the free market economics of today. We need to face the truth.

Social and ethical values no longer constrain the expression of selfishness. The society of Smith's day was weak on economics — hunger, disease, and early death were common — but it had a strong cultural and moral foundation. However, that social and ethical foundation has been seriously eroded over the past 200 years by the glorification of greed. Civil litigation and criminal prosecution seem to be the only limits to unethical and immoral pursuit of profit and growth. Concerns of today's wealthy for today's poor seem to be limited to concerns that welfare benefits may be too high or that they will be mugged or robbed if the poor become too desperate. Smith's defense of the pursuit of self-interest must be reconsidered within the context of today's society — a society that is now strong on economics but weak on community and morality. We need to face the truth.

The economic theories of two centuries ago are no longer relevant to the world of today. The pursuit of greed no longer creates societal good — it simply encourages more greed. The greedy now have control of the economy and much of society. And they won't give up without a fight. It's time for a new revolution in America, a revolution that will free people from the tyranny of the economics of individual, short-run self-interest. The new revolution will require a rethinking of and a direct challenge to the fundamental principles that underlie conventional economic thinking — line by line, row by row, from the ground up. Any effort that fails to attack the problem at its root cause ultimately is destined to fail. The root cause of the current crisis in agriculture is the same as the root cause of ecological degradation and of social and moral decay of society in general

— a society that blindly accepts the economic bottom line as if it were the word of God. It's time to face up to the truth in America. The time for quietness has passed.

This new American Revolution is being fomented under the conceptual umbrella of "sustainability." In farming, we talk about the sustainable agriculture movement, but there are also movements in sustainable forestry, sustainable communities, sustainable development, and sustainable society in general. The sustainability movement presents a direct challenge to conventional economic thinking. Sustainability includes concern for self-interests, but it goes beyond to protecting interests that are shared with others, and the interests of future generations in which we have not even a share. All of the sustainability movements share a common goal, to meet the needs of the present while leaving equal or better opportunities for those to follow — to apply the Golden Rule across generations.

There is a growing consensus among those marching under the banner of sustainability that for anything to be sustainable it must be ecologically sound, economically viable, and socially responsible. All three are necessary and none alone or no pair of two is sufficient. Economic viability is about self-interest, social responsibility is a matter of shared interest, and ecological soundness ultimately is an ethical or moral responsibility that we choose to accept for purely altruistic reasons. Self-interest, shared interests, and altruistic interests are all considered positive and worthy of pursuit. Thus, the pursuit of sustainability is a pursuit of more "enlightened self-interests." Without this enlightenment, we will not choose long-run sustainability over short-run greed.

The sustainability revolution is not one that will be fought on the battlefield, in the streets, or even necessarily in the halls of Congress. Instead, it's a battle for the hearts and minds of the American people. We need to tell people the truth about what is happening in America today and why. We need to tell them the truth about the need for a new economics of sustainability — an economics that will sustain people and protect the environment, not just promote industrial development and economic growth. And we need to give them common sense reasons why the old system cannot be sustained, and why a new sustainable system is not a luxury but an absolute necessity. We need to talk boldly about the need for a new economics of enlightenment. The time for quietness has passed.

Agriculture may well be the field upon which the battle for the hearts and minds of Americans is first fought. The best hope for building a sustainable society may be to begin by building a more sustainable agriculture — for without a sustainable agriculture, human life on earth is not sustainable. The best hope for building a more sustainable agriculture may be to begin by ensuring the future of small farm families — for without farmers, agriculture cannot be sustained. Corporate hired hands may be good people, fully deserving of dignity and respect, but they are not farmers. A corporately controlled, large-scale, industrial agriculture simply is not sustainable.

Sustainable farms will not only be independently owned but they also will be smaller farms. Sustainable farming is a product of balance and harmony, among the ecological, economic, and social dimensions of farming systems. A smaller farm lacking this harmony is less likely to be sustainable than a larger farm that is more in harmony. But there are logical reasons to believe the necessary balance and harmony will be far easier to achieve with a large number of smaller farms rather than a small number of large farms.

Nature is inherently diverse. Geographic regions are different, watersheds are different, farms are different, and fields are even different — both among and within. Industrial agriculture treats fields, farms, watersheds, and even regions as if they were all pretty much the same. Certainly, industrial systems can be fine-tuned a bit here and there to make production practices of one region fit another. Each state has a bit different set of best management practices, and some further adjustments are made from farm to farm and field to field. But the basic systems of conventional agricultural production are all pretty much the same.

The same breeds and varieties, fertilizers and feeds, pesticides and antibiotics, machinery and equipment, and business and marketing strategies are used across fields, farms, and watersheds, in all regions of the country. The goal of current agricultural research is to find universal solutions to common problems — to find ways to twist, bend, and force nature to conform to some universal production and distribution process. Industrial, large-scale mass production requires uniformity. Biotechnology is but the latest in a long string of futile efforts to force uniformity upon nature.

But nature is diverse. Large-scale production systems create inherent conflicts with the diversity of nature and inherently threaten sustainability. Farms that conform to their ecological niches avoid such conflicts. Some ecological niches may be large, but most are quite small. Current concerns for agricultural sustainability are based on strong and growing evidence that most farms have already outgrown their ecological niches and could be more sustainable if they were smaller.

Sustainable farms must also be of a size consistent with their markets. Conventional wisdom is that most markets are mass markets, and thus, farms must be large, or if not, must market their production collectively. The conventional wisdom is wrong. Markets are made up of individual consumers, and as consumers — as people — we are all different. We don't all want the same things. In fact, each of us actually prefers something just a bit different, and thus, values the same things a bit differently.

Mass markets were created by lumping together a lot of people who were willing to accept the same basic things, even though they might have preferred something else. If mass markets could be created, the food system could be industrialized, and dollar and cent food costs would be lower. The lower price bribed consumers to accept something other than what they actually preferred. Typically, consumers must be coerced as well as bribed to accept what the industrial system has to offer. That's why Americans spend more for advertising and packaging of food than they pay the farmer to produce it. It costs more to convince people to buy industrial food products than it does to produce them.

Eighty cents of each dollar spent for food goes for processing, transportation, packaging, advertising, and other marketing services. One key to economic sustainability of small farms is to capture a larger share of the consumers' food dollar by performing some, and bypassing others, of these marketing services. Farmers currently keep less than half of the amount they get from each food dollar as a return for what they contribute to production; the other half goes for purchased inputs. By tailoring production to consumer niche markets, and selling more directly to consumers, small farmers have opportunities to make bigger profits without becoming big farmers.

The conventional wisdom is that niche-marketing opportunities are limited and can support only a handful of farmers. Once again, the conventional wisdom is wrong. Since all people want something slightly different, the ultimate in niche marketing would be to give every individual precisely what they want. All consumer markets are made up of individuals — totally, not just in part. Thus, all mass markets are made up of many small niche markets. The question is not how many niches exist, but instead how many different niches does it make sense to serve? The relevant answer, at least at present, is that more than enough market niches exist to support as many small farmers as might choose to market directly to consumers. A lack of niche markets need not place a lower limit on the size of farms. Farms can be as many and as small as needed to accommodate the ecological niches of nature.

The most compelling argument in support of sustainable farms being smaller is that sustainable farms must be managed more "intensively." Wendell Berry puts it most succinctly in his book, *What Are People For?*, "... if agriculture is to remain productive, it must preserve the land and the fertility and ecological health of the land; the land, that is, must be used well. A further requirement, therefore, is that if the land is to be used well, the people who use it must know it well, must be highly motivated to use it well, must know how to use it well, must have time to use it well, and must be able to afford to use it well." Intensive management is possible only if farmers have an intensive relationship with the land — if they know it, care about it, know how to care for it, take time to care for it, and can afford to care for it, only if they love it.

Industrialization degrades and destroys the relationship between the farmer and the land. Industrialization is management *extensive.* Specialization, standardization, and centralization allow each farmer to cover more land, supervise more workers, and handle more dollars. Industrial management is extensive in that each manager is able to manage more resources. Extensive management makes it possible for each farmer to make more profits in total, even if profits per unit of production are less. But as the attention of individual farmers is spread over more land, more laborers, and more capital, each acre of land, each worker, and each dollar invested receives less personal attention. The relationship of the farmer with the land, and with the people of the land, is weakened. If those on large farms no longer know the land, no longer care about it, forget how to care for it, don't have time to care for it, or can't afford to care about it, how well will the land be used? How can it remain productive? How can a large farm be sustained?

A small farm can be managed *intensively.* Intensive management allows a farmer to manage less land, using less labor while handling fewer dollars. By managing fewer resources more intensively, the farmer is able to make more profit per unit of output, and thus, make more total profits, even if total production or output is less. As the farmer has more time and attention to give to each acre of land, each worker, and each dollar invested, the farmer's relationship to the land and the people of the land is strengthened. The small farmer has an opportunity to know the land, to care about it, to learn how to care for it, has time to care for it, and can afford to care about it. The land on a small farm can be used well and can remain sustainably productive.

The fundamental purpose of farming is to harvest solar energy — to transform sunlight into food and fiber for human use. It might seem that even God favors the larger farmer because large farms cover more space and thus catch more sunshine and rain. But God also has given us a choice of making either wise or foolish use of the gifts of nature with which we are entrusted. Our industrial food system requires ten calories of fossil energy, in addition to the solar energy, for each calorie of food energy it produces. This can hardly be deemed a wise and efficient use of energy. But as a consequence, a small farmer can be more economically, socially, and ecologically viable than a large farm, simply by being a more effective harvester of the solar energy. In essence, a more intensive manager is a better harvester of the sun.

Some ecosystems and farming systems are easier to manage effectively than are others, and thus, require less attention per unit of resources to manage sustainably. Those requiring less intensive management can be larger without sacrificing sustainability. For example, a sustainable wheat/forage/cattle farm may be far larger than a sustainable vegetable/berry/poultry farm. But the sustainable wheat/forage/cattle farm is likely to be far smaller than the typical specialized wheat farm, forage farm, or cattle ranch. And the sustainable vegetable/berry/poultry farm is likely to be far smaller than the typical specialized vegetable farm, berry farm, or poultry operation.

Sustainable farms need not be small in terms of acres farmed or total production, but they will need to be managed intensively. And intensively managed farms will be smaller than will otherwise similar farms that are managed extensively. Neither land nor people can be sustained unless they are given the attention, care, and affection they need to survive, thrive, and prosper. The necessary attention, care, and affection are easier to give on a smaller farm than on a larger farm.

The best alternatives for American farmers are neither to get bigger, give in to corporate control, nor to get out of farming. The best alternative for American farmers and for society in general is for farmers to find ways to farm more sustainably — to balance economic, ecological, and social concerns, to find harmony among self-interests, shared interests, and altruism, to pursue enlightened self-interests instead of greed. American farmers need to be told the truth about their alternatives. Farms of the future must be smaller, not larger. It's time for a revolution in American agriculture. The time for quietness has passed.

About a year and a half ago, I found myself recovering from unanticipated open-heart surgery. I was fortunate enough to have previously checked out a book, *The Life and Major Works of Thomas Paine*. Thomas Paine, as you may recall from your history lessons, was a writer during the American Revolution. He was credited with articulating the ideas of the revolution in terms that could be understood by the *common man*. In fact, he signed his early writings with the pen name "Common Sense." Paine's pamphlets were distributed widely throughout the colonies, and invariably regenerated public support for the cause of democracy, saving the revolution from failure on more than one occasion. The writings of Thomas Paine provide some valuable insights into how to keep a revolution from failing — at least when the cause makes common sense.

First, Paine gave no quarter to the enemy of American freedom and democracy — the British monarchy. Nothing in Paine's writings could be mistaken for impartial objectivity when he was critiquing the sins of the monarchy. He stuck with facts and stated the truth, but he bothered with only one set of facts and one side of the truth. He left out some of the facts, the other side of the truth, but left the lies to be told by his opponents.

Second, Paine's writing always went beyond criticism. He always went on to extol the great benefits that would be realized by the colonies once they had shed the yoke of Great Britain. He painted a vision for the future of a free and democratic America. He countered each British claim of what the colonies would lose with a counter-claim of what the colonies would gain once they had won the revolution.

Finally, Paine's writings never gave as much as a hint of doubt that the American colonists eventually would win their war for independence. When the British army occupied Philadelphia, for example, Paine called it clear and convincing evidence that the British could never win the war. If half of their army was required to hold just one town, how could they possibly control all of the vast regions of the American colonies? It was just plain *common sense,* the cause of the revolution could not be denied.

We need a Thomas Paine approach to the new movement to revolutionize American society. I am not talking about gradual, incremental change in practices and methods of doing business; I am talking about a fundamentally different philosophy of life. The differences between the industrial and a post-industrial society will be as great as the differences between monarchy and democracy.

The current enemy in not a misguided monarchy, but instead is a misguided economy. The tyranny is not a *kingdom*, but instead is the *marketplace*. The epitome of the economics of greed is the publicly held industrial corporation. The publicly held corporation has no heart, it has no soul, and it is motivated solely by profit and growth. Corporations pollute and waste natural resources, they degrade and use up people, and they corrupt any political process that attempts to keep them from doing either. Anything that has no value in the market place is worthless to the corporation. The people who choose to work for corporations have no choice but to feed the unending corporate hunger for ever greater profits and ever faster growth.

Corporate industrialization will do for agriculture as it has done for other sectors of the economy. It will pollute the natural environment — the water, the soil, and the air. The natural productivity of the land eventually will be depleted. Farmer and farm workers, like factory workers, will suffer ill health, low pay, and eventual abandonment — as agribusinesses find other people in other places who will work even harder, in more dangerous environments, for even less pay. The safety and healthfulness of the food supply will continue to deteriorate as a consequence of the inevitable *race to the bottom,* to see which corporation can produce the most *stuff* cheapest. However, once they have driven their competitors out of business, they will be free to raise prices to whatever level they choose.

The industrial era is over. The era of information and knowledge is upon us. Knowledge and information are quickly replacing capital as the source of new productivity and wealth. Potential productivity is now embodied in the unique ability of people to think and create, not in raw materials and factories. The main reason corporations continue to consolidate and grow is to gain greater economic and political power — to exploit workers, taxpayers, and consumers so they can continue to show profits and grow. In the industrial era, bigger was accepted as better, but in the new post-industrial era, small will be smarter. We are living in a new era of human and economic development.

Small businesses allow people to express their individuality and creativity — to use their unique abilities to think and create. The good paying new jobs in the general economy are being created by small businesses, while the old industrial giants continue to downsize and layoff workers by the thousands. If the future is to be better than the past, it must belong to the small, not the large. The future of farming belongs to the small farms, not to the large. The people need to be told the truth.

Small farms allow people to fit their uniqueness to their ecological niche and to the unique tastes and preferences of consumers. Small farms are management intensive — they allow farmers to rely more on themselves and less on borrowed capital and rented land. Intensive management allows farmers to break away from chronic crisis — to get off the treadmill of larger and fewer which requires the survivors to run faster and faster just to stay in the same place. Small farms can be *real* farms — where farmers have the time and the money to take care of their families, their land, and their communities. Small farms allow people to live in harmony again, with themselves, their neighbors, and the things of nature. Small farms can be farmed sustainably, thus benefiting farm families, rural communities, the natural environment, and society in general.

There is a better way to farm and a better way to live. It's time for a revolution in American agriculture. The time for quietness has passed.

Sustainability requires diversity, flexibility, site specificity, and decentralized decision making. Farms of the future must be as small as the ecological niches to which they must conform to be in harmony with the diversity of nature. Farms of the future must be as small as the market niches to which they must conform to be in harmony with the diversity of human nature. The only farms with a future will be farms that are sustainable — that are economically viable, ecologically sound, and socially responsible. The inevitability of the industrialization of agriculture is a lie. Sustainable small farms are better alternatives than getting bigger, giving in, or getting out. The American public must be told the truth. It's time for a small farm revolution in America. The time for quietness has passed.

1999

02 | Small Farms: Perceptions versus Realities

*P*eople who choose to live and work on small farms face a number of unnecessary obstacles as they pursue their chosen way of life. In general, these obstacles arise from misperceptions on the part of those in the agricultural establishment — those who make public policies or provide public services pertaining to agriculture.

Perception: Small farms are not really a significant part of American agriculture. Government farm programs for the past several decades have been driven by concerns for production rather than people. The underlying assumption has been that the public would benefit most by focusing on improving the efficiency of farming, ultimately bringing down the cost of food and fiber to consumers. This focus on efficiency is the root cause of the trend toward larger, more specialized farming operations. Today, the USDA and Land Grant Universities are promoting high-tech and biotech production for the same reason — cheap food for consumers.

Reality: Small farms are a significant part of American agriculture. While a focus on production may have been a legitimate orientation in the past, there is no longer any significant benefit to be gained from increasing the productive efficiency of agriculture. First, the American consumer no longer spends 40%–50% of their income for food, as they did when the USDA and Land Grants were established, but instead spends a little more than 10 percent — a dime of each dollar and the farmer only gets about a penny from that dime. The rest goes for farm inputs and marketing costs. Even if farming were perfectly efficient, if farming cost nothing, consumers would only save a dime of each dollar spent for food. Further improvements in the efficiency of farming simply cannot make food much cheaper. Consumers no longer benefit from making farms bigger.

Perception: Small farmers are not real farmers. Most small farms are part-time farms; many are nothing more than rural residences with a garden or a few head of livestock. Others are strictly hobby farmers with no intention of earning a farm income. Some so-called farmers actually are urban residents who own land in the country. While living in the country or owning land may be important to these people, they are not *real farmers.*

Reality: Most real farmers are small farmers. Admittedly, many of those census entities counted as farms are hobby farmers and rural residences. But many are not. The census asks farmers to provide their primary occupation — the occupation at which they spend more than half of their working hours. When considering only those whose primary occupation is farming, and who are not retired, more than half of these *real farmers* would easily be classified as small farmers. Well over half of these *primary-occupation* farmers have less than $100,000 in annual gross sales, and nearly half have gross sales of less than $50,000 per year.

Perception: A family can't depend on a small farm for a significant part of their living. There is no way that a farm with gross sales of less than $50,000 a year can be a serious commercial operation. Farmer's net incomes generally run about 10 to 20 percent of gross sales, even on well-managed small farms, and $7,000 to $10,000 a year certainly won't support a family. The only hope for farm families grossing less than $100,000 per year is to rely on non-farm sources for most of their income. Those grossing between $100,000 and $250,000 are not really small farms, but are middle-sized farms on their way to getting big.

Reality: A small farm can support a family. Successful small farmers pursue a fundamentally different approach to farming than do big farmers. They reduce their reliance on purchased inputs by substituting labor and management for capital and purchased inputs — they are low-input farmers. They focus on creating value, as well as reducing costs — they are niche-marketers. They give individual consumers what they want, rather than produce bulk commodities for mass markets. They do the things they do best, the things they have a passion for, and as a consequence, do them better. They build relationships with their customers, and thus, are less vulnerable to the ups and downs of commodity prices. As a result of all these things, these small farmers can earn far greater income per dollar of sales than do conventional large farmers. A farm with $50,000 gross sales may well contribute $25,000 or more to support the family; a farm with gross sales of $100,000 can be a full-time family farm.

Perception: Many small farms earn little if any net income. Many small farms report no net farm income, and thus, are an economic burden rather than an asset — or perhaps a luxury that many small farm families cannot afford. For those who are actually trying to make a living on small farms and are failing; this is a public welfare issue, not an agricultural issue. Farm programs were never intended to be rural welfare programs.

Reality: Small farms that report little if any net income may still be very important economically to small farm families. First, many families on small farms live simply. They do not live in poverty, but their *economic* standard of living is not as high as that of their urban neighbors. To them, farming is truly a way of life as well as a business. The farm provides them with a home, much of their food, a good place to raise their family, a place for recreation and relaxation, and a place for learning and teaching — as well as a place to work. Many of these smaller farms are not obligated to report any net income from farming because many of the costs of living on a farm qualify as "farm costs." Many small farms, if they are part-time farms, need not earn an income; their non-market value to the family is sufficient to justify the farming operation.

Perception: Technologies are scale neutral. Technologies developed for larger, commercial farming operations are equally useful on small farms. After all, the only way for a small farm to survive and succeed is for it to get larger — to grow to a size appropriate to use technologies more efficiently. And for those who can afford to farm as a hobby, they surely want access to the best technology available. What difference does it make to a cow whether she is in a herd of ten or ten thousand? Her needs are still the same. What difference does it make to a corn plant whether it is in a field of ten or ten thousand acres? Its needs are still the same. If the scale of technology doesn't matter to the animal or plant, it is of no consequence to the farmer.

Reality: Technologies are not scale-neutral. Industrial technologies developed for larger, commercial farming operations are not appropriate for small farms. Agricultural technologies of the past have provided means of specializing and standardizing production processes, thus industrializing the management function and allowing farms to grow larger.

Successful small farms must be management intensive — they must earn more returns per acre, per dollar invested, per dollar-value of production. The higher returns to management from intensively managed farms comes from the efficiency with which the various practices, methods, and enterprises on the farm are integrated together — not necessarily from the efficiency of each individual practice, method, or enterprise. A cow or a stalk of corn has a very different role in a diversified, integrated small farm system than in a large, specialized beef herd or corn farm. Small farmers need research and technology that will enhance their human capacity to manage things — to understand, to think. They need technologies that will allow them to manage *more intensively.*

Perception: Existing publicly funded programs are adequately meeting the legitimate needs of small farmers. The public agencies, like the USDA and Land Grant Universities, contend that those who complain about inadequate attention to small farm issues are simply living in the past when small farms were actually economically viable. Progress in the agricultural economy, by necessity, has left small farmers behind. There is nothing that government could do to roll back or even slow the technological advances of large-scale agriculture, even if it could justify doing so. Small farm advocates are simply out of touch with today's reality.

Reality: Publicly funded programs are not adequately meeting the legitimate needs of small farmers. Small farmers have found ways to survive and persist in spite of the lack of research and educational support, and in spite of government programs that have supported and promoted large farms and corporate agriculture competitors. Small farmers, using any reasonable definition, make up more than half of all primary occupation farmers. This is not a fantasy; this is a statistical fact. These are not farmers of the past, these are farmers of the present, and they deserve the respect and attention of their public institutions.

Small farm advocates are in touch with the realities of today, but perhaps more important, they are looking to the future. They are not opposed to technology; they simply want technologies that are consistent with long-run sustainability as well as short-run profitability. The future of human civilization depends not only upon food, but also on a healthy environment and a civilized human society. There is no better means of sustaining human life on earth than to have people on the land who are intellectually capable, socially responsible, and ethically committed to meeting the needs of both present and future generations through farming. An industrial agriculture is not sustainable. There can be no better investment of public dollars than in keeping the land in the hands of small farmers who are committed to the sustainability of agriculture.

2000

03 | Farmers Are Fighting Back

*A*fter decades of betrayal by the agricultural establishment, farmers are finally beginning to fight back. For decades, so-called producers' associations have been promoting the industrialization of agriculture, which has contributed directly to the demise of the producers who have been paying for their programs. Over the past decade, for example, the Missouri Pork Producers Association has been promoting large-scale corporate hog operation through their support of industrial research and market development programs. During this same time, the number of hogs produced in Missouri has risen dramatically with the influx of large corporate operations, but the number of Missouri hog farmers has dropped to less than a third of previous levels. But, the nation's hog farmers have voted to abolish the national pork check-off program, which supports the Missouri and National Pork Producers Councils. Farmers are finally beginning to fight back.

The check-offs are based on a percentage of the total sales value of hogs. Thus, the so-called producers' organizations are concerned about the total number of hogs sold, not about the number of hog producers. They cater to the large-scale corporate operations and support their takeover of the hog/pork sector because those operations sell more hogs and generate more check-off dollars. So, smaller family hog farmers end up subsidizing the same corporate operations that are driving them out of business. But farmers have begun to fight back. Cattlemen are following the hog farmers' lead, and are petitioning USDA for a vote on the beef check-off program as well. Hopefully, farmers won't stop fighting back until they have eliminated all subsidies for these corporate operations that are destroying family farms and rural communities as they foul the natural environment.

I heard the results of the pork check-off vote while attending a meeting of farmers and rural activists who have been opposing corporate takeover of hog production. More than 500 people from all across the country attended a "Sustainable Hog Farming Summit" in New Bern, NC. The Water Keepers Alliance was one of the sponsors. Under the leadership of Robert Kennedy, Jr., the Alliance has assembled a team of powerful law firms that are committed to forcing large-scale corporate hog operations to comply with the Federal Clean Water Act, and other federal laws protecting the natural environment. These are the same law firms that have successfully sued the asbestos industry, the tobacco industry, and the pharmaceutical industry for knowingly destroying the health of millions of people. These firms are now ready to take on the corporate hog industry for knowingly degrading the natural environment and threatening the health of millions of people who live "downstream or downwind" from factory hog operations.

Up to now, the grassroots family farm and rural advocacy groups had been no match for large agribusiness corporations, either in the courts or in the halls of Congress. Now, however, advocates for sustainable family farms and rural communities will be supported by a group of well-financed, committed advocates for a clean rural environment. The farmers who fight back now have a good change of winning.[1]

Many farmers, however, are still unwittingly supporting corporate agriculture when they oppose enforcement of environmental and health regulations. Farmers need to realize that these large-scale corporate operations would lose much, if not all, of their cost advantage over family farms if they were forced to protect the environment by properly disposing of their wastes. It's far easier and less costly to handle wastes properly and to protect the environment in a smaller-scale, diversified hog operation. Perhaps some specific rules and regulations need to be changed to reflect the smaller environmental risks from smaller, less concentrated animal production, but farmers who oppose enforcement of environmental protection laws in general are helping the corporations put family farmers out of business. The Water Keepers group is not just anti-corporate agriculture; they are pro-family farming because they believe that family

[1] This effort was undermined by the change in administration of the U.S. Environmental Protection Agency (Robert F. Kennedy, Jr., *Crimes Against Nature*, Harper Collins, 2004, pages 74-75).

farmers want to be good stewards of the environment. The family farmers fighting corporate hog operations need help, rather than opposition, from their neighbors.

Farmers also are beginning to fight back on a number of other fronts. Many farmers are beginning to realize that the so-called farmers' cooperatives have become virtually identical to the corporations against which they were supposed to protect farmers. These cooperatives no longer support farmers but instead support the industrialization process that is forcing farmers out of business. A true farmers' cooperative helps farmers make profits, instead of making profits for the cooperative that rarely find their way back to farmers. The giant national dairy cooperatives, for example, have driven thousands of family dairy farmers out of business by using the same business tactics as agribusiness corporations. Farm supply and marketing cooperatives, such as Missouri Farmers Association, have abandoned the cause of family farmers and now openly promote and support agricultural industrialization. Too often, the new "closed membership cooperatives" turn out to be nothing more than ways for wealthy farmers to invest venture capital. But more and more farmers are abandoning "farmers' cooperatives" that don't support farmers and are searching for ways to fight back.

Farmers are also beginning to fight back against general farm organizations, such as the Farm Bureau Federation, that support the industrialization of agriculture to the detriment of farmers. A farm organization cannot have millions of dollars invested in agribusiness corporations, such as Continental Grain, IBP, and Premium Standard Farms, and effectively represent the farmers who are routinely squeezed out of business by these same corporations. The policy agenda supported by such farm organizations in Washington, D.C. is not an agenda designed to maintain family farms, but instead is an agenda to maximize agricultural production. Maximum agricultural production keeps farm-level prices depressed, weakens bargaining power of farmers, and maximizes profits of marketing and processing firms. Policies that have driven farmers out of business have been supported by so-called farm organizations that claim to speak for farmers.

However, farmers have begun to fight back. The National Farmers Union, an organization with a long history of advocacy of family farms, has begun to openly oppose the industrial agriculture policies of the Farm Bureau and the various farm commodity groups. The President of the National Farmers Union announced the defeat of the national pork check-off at the Hog Summit in North Carolina and openly proclaimed it as a victory for family hog farmers. The Farmers Union is an old organization nationally, but has organized in Missouri only within the past few years. Their membership is growing as more and more farmers fight back.

Farmers are also are fighting back against the U.S. Department of Agriculture — against their support to industrial agriculture. A group of African-American farmers recently won a multimillion-dollar lawsuit against the USDA for discriminatory practices in implementation of government programs — specifically, in administration of government farm loans. The Organization of Competitive Markets is a newly formed group organized by commercial farmers and livestock feeders who are challenging USDA and the Department of Justice for failing to enforce antitrust regulations against corporate monopolization of agricultural markets. Organic farmers' groups from all across the country forced USDA to withdraw and rewrite proposed standards for organic production that would have favored large-scale, corporate producers. Farmers of all kinds all across the country are beginning to fight back against government programs that support agricultural industrialization.

Farmers have not yet begun to fight back against their Land Grant Universities — at least not effectively. One after another, the major Land Grant Universities have sold out family farmers to agricultural industrialization. Publicly funded research and extension programs have supported and promoted specialization, standardization, and consolidation of decision making as a means of making agriculture more efficient. As farms have become more specialized and standardized, management has been consolidated among fewer decision makers, meaning that farming operations become larger in size and fewer in numbers. Industrialization, by its very nature, forces family farmers out of business and promotes the eventual corporate control of agriculture. In recent years, however, universities have begun to even brag about the "partnerships" they are forming with the giant agribusiness corporations that are forcing family farmers out of business. Yet most farmers continue to support their universities, perhaps out of blind loyalty, or maybe in disbelief that "their university" could possibly betray them.

In the mid-1990s, several Land Grant Universities reluctantly recognized the legitimate demands of small farmers, organic farmers, and family farmers who had rejected the industrial model, by initiating small programs in sustainable agriculture. However, many of these universities are now downsizing or eliminating their sustainable agriculture programs. The University of Missouri is no exception. Universities seem to be afraid that sustainable agriculture programs might tarnish their image with the corporate industries they have come to rely on for political and financial support. They have been told by their corporate supporters that biotechnology is the only way we can produce enough to feed the world. They have become so preoccupied with increasing production, or perhaps with maintaining corporate support, that they have forgotten about their responsibility for serving the people. Perhaps the universities will be forced to refocus when more farmers begin fighting back.

Farmers who now realize that an industrial agriculture destroys family farms, rural communities, and the natural environment are fighting back. Farmers who realize that making money, while necessary, just isn't enough are fighting back. They are committed to caring for the land and caring about other people. Farmers are fighting back because they now realize that the only way to truly sustain agriculture is to sustain people through agriculture.

2001

The Colonization of Rural America

04

ural America is being "colonized." Multinational corporations are extending their economic sovereignty over the affairs of people in rural places everywhere, including rural America. Rural people are losing control of their local public institutions as outside corporate interests, previously alien to their communities, use their economic power to gain controlling influence over local governments. Irreplaceable precious rural resources, including rural people and rural culture, are being exploited to increase the wealth of investors and managers of corporations that have no commitment to the future of their "rural colonies." This is a classic colonization.

Historically, a colony has been defined as a territory, acquired by conquest or settlement, over which a people or government, previously alien to that territory, has imposed outside control. A colonial relationship existed whenever one people or government extended its sovereignty by imposing political control over another people or territory. The only fundamental difference between the current colonization of rural areas and previous colonization of "lesser developed" countries is the nature of the entity carrying out the process — the source of power. Historically, colonization has been carried out by political entities, by governments. Today, colonization is being carried out by economic entities, by multinational corporations. However, the colonization process and its consequences are virtually identical, regardless of the source of power.

Rural people, whether in America or elsewhere, are being told that they must rely on outside investment to support local economic development.

Outside investment will bring badly needed jobs and income, stimulate the local economy, and expand the local tax base. Economically depressed rural communities will be able to afford better schools, better health care, and expanded social services, and will attract a greater variety of retail outlets — restaurants, movie theaters, and maybe even a Wal Mart. Their rural community will begin to look more like an urban community and local people can begin to think and act more like urban people. Rural people have been left behind, they are told, and outside investment is the only means by which they can advance fast enough to catch up with the rest of society.

These same basic arguments have been used by the powerful of all times to justify their colonization of the weak. Colonization was the only feasible means of improving the lives of the "natives" left behind in "primitive" societies — economically, socially, and morally. Since the indigenous people had no adequate means of developing their resources themselves, it was only fair they give up some of the benefits to the colonizing nation in order to acquire the outside investment needed for the development process. It was a "win-win" situation, so they were told.

Historically, the British, Spanish, Portuguese, French, Germans, and Dutch were among the great empire builders. They colonized much of North, South, and Central America, Australia, and Africa, as well as major regions of Asia. Through colonization, the "primitive" people already occupying these territories were given an opportunity to become a part of a modern society. After failing to gain cooperation through persuasion, the leaders of the indigenous tribes were invariably bribed, threatened, or coerced into colluding with the colonizing powers. After all, it was for the ultimate good of the "their people." The 19th century empire builders, in particular, claimed they had a moral responsibility to help bring "backward people" some of the fruits of modern Western Civilization. And, if the natives continued to resist, they were subdued by force and their indigenous cultures destroyed — for their own good, of course.

Clearly, becoming part of a colonial empire brought numerous economic, health, education, and technological benefits to past colonies. In some cases, such as North America and Australia, the indigenous population was sufficiently small to be essentially eliminated by colonizing immigrants. Some colonies became strong enough to gain independence and a few are now more powerful than are their one-time masters. But most colonies were not granted independence until well into the 20th century when world opinion shifted against colonialism on ethical and moral grounds.

According to contemporary standards of international behavior, colonialism is inexcusable because it conflicts directly with the basic rights of national sovereignty and self-determination. The recognition of such rights, worldwide, ended political colonialism as a means of promoting economic and cultural development. Political colonialism was abolished worldwide, because it had obvious harmful effects on the people of colonized areas — socially, culturally, ecologically, and economically. Long established social life-styles were suddenly disrupted, complete cultures were destroyed, natural resources were depleted, and the natural environment was polluted with industrial chemicals and toxic wastes. And, after the colonizers had completed their exploitation, the local economy was left in shambles with no indigenous community structure or any other means of self-government to address the shameful legacy of colonialism. In spite of the obvious economic and technological benefits of colonization, the indigenous people of virtually every previously colonized country of the world, including the United States, still harbor a deep resentment of their former colonial masters. Political colonization is no longer morally or ethically excusable.

However, the "corporate colonization" of rural areas everywhere, including in America, continues virtually unchecked. The earliest colonial intrusions into rural America were motivated by exploitation of its abundant wildlife, vast forestlands, and precious minerals deposits, invariably leaving behind frontier "ghost towns" after the wealth had been extracted from the land. More recently, intrusions have been motivated by the exploitation of cheap rural labor, by the textile and food processing industries, for example. But, once the corporations found people who would work even harder for less money in other countries, the textile industry moved on, leaving behind deserted factories and unemployable people. With the creation of the North American Free Trade Agreement, the food processing industry now seems likely to abandon North America to colonize rural Mexico instead. However, corporate colonialism continues in rural America. Many rural areas are still being colonized to exploit remaining pockets of valuable rural resources, including an agricultural work ethic, trusting communities, and open spaces in which to dump various kinds of noxious wastes, which urban people have rejected.

Today, giant factory hog operations provide a prime example of corporate colonization of rural America. Local people are promised new jobs, more income, an expanded tax base, and an opportunity to "catch up" with the rest of American society. Local leaders are courted or coerced, as necessary, to shape local policies to accommodate industrial hog production methods. Local farmers are told industrialization is the wave of the future for agriculture and they must embrace the new technologies to survive. Rural people are told that local regulations to protect the public health and natural environment will drive existing farmers out of business, will stifle economic development, and will doom their community to continued "backwardness." These arguments are no different from past arguments used to support political colonization; only the source of power is different.

In reality, few local people will gain anything from this new colonization. A few local officials and land speculators may line their pockets, and a few local people may get relatively good paying jobs, for a time. But nearly all of the profits and good paying jobs will go to corporate investors and managers who will remain outside the community. Most rural Americans eventually will refuse to work for exploitative employers, leaving most of the low-paying jobs to be filled by immigrant labor. Eventually, the colonizing corporations will move on, once local resources have been depleted or local resistance to their exploitation begins to affect their bottom line. Perhaps some post-colonial rural communities will be prosperous, but these so-called success stories will be limited to places with unique landscapes and climates deemed worthy of preserving for the enjoyment of affluent outsiders.

As in earlier times, the 21st century corporate empire builders claim they feel some responsibility to help bring "backward people" of rural areas some of the benefits of the modern economy. However, rural people are not necessarily "backward," just because they have not embraced the exploitative system of industrial development and have been reluctant to discard their traditional rural cultural values. After the corporations are gone, there is no reason to believe that rural Americans will be less resentful of their previous "colonial masters" than are indigenous people of previously colonized nations. They will resent the loss of rural culture, rural values, and their previous sense of connectedness to place. They will resent the loss of a once safe and healthy rural environment in which they had hoped to live and raise their families. They will resent the loss of their self-governing ability as their communities will have been split apart by dissention during the colonizing process. They will resent the loss of their sense of community.

The threat of colonization is always present. The economically and politically powerful will always be tempted to dominate and exploit the weak. However, differences in economic and political power only make colonization possible — not necessary or inevitable. The powerful can be restrained from their natural tendency to expand their sovereignty over the weak, and even if they are not, the weak can always find ways to resist the powerful.

The strongest defense rural America has against the threat of corporate colonization is the knowledge of what is happening to their communities, why it is happening, and what are the consequences of their doing nothing to stop it. The colonization of rural America is not inevitable. But, rural Americans must stand together to preserve their priceless rural culture, to protect their valuable natural and human resources, and pursue a different strategy of "sustainable" rural economic development.

2002

05 | The Rights of Rural Americans

C hanges in agriculture are raising new questions regarding the rights of all rural Americans. Historically, farmers have defended their "right to farm," whenever residential development has brought in urban neighbors with no appreciation for the normal sights, sounds, and smells of farming. More recently, rural residents have claimed their "right of self-defense" against growing threats to their health, safety, and welfare brought on by new industrial farming methods, particularly large-scale confinement animal feeding operations (CAFOs).

Rural residents have argued with increasing success that industrial agriculture is not farming, at least not the type of farming protected by right to farm laws. Instead, they claim that CAFOs represent the unwelcome intrusion of a dangerous, obnoxious industry into their communities. The agricultural establishment has responded with widespread efforts to restrict or deny the rights of rural communities to impose any higher standards for protection of public health and the environment than that required by state law. Such initiatives have been promoted in Missouri, Pennsylvania, North Dakota, Kentucky, and undoubtedly other states of which I am not personally aware. A similar initiative at the national level seeks to prevent states from adopting restrictions on agriculture that go beyond those imposed by federal law. The fundamental questions seem to be whether local communities have the right to exceed state standards in protecting their health and environment, and whether states have the right to exceed federal standards. The answers boil down to a matter of rights.

Questions of pubic rights can be resolved most clearly by relating them to personal rights. After all, government — whether local, state, or national — is simply the means by which we formalize our relationships whenever the numbers of people involved are too large to resolve matters personally. Similar questions of rights and responsibilities arise anytime people relate to each other — whether within nations, communities, or families. It's just easier to see the logical answers to such questions in personal relationships among family members.

The federal government has the right to set minimum standards of acceptable conduct, as required to protect our constitutional rights. All rights not granted to the federal government by the Constitution are reserved for the states. States obviously are not limited to enforcing the federal minimums for acceptable conduct. In fact, the vast majority of all criminal and civil laws are state laws. State laws cannot conflict with federal laws but may go far beyond the federal minimums when necessary to protect and promote the well-being of a state's residents. People within families and communities have a responsibility to conform to both state and federal minimum standards of conduct; otherwise, they are breaking the law. It also seems logical and reasonable that families and communities have every right to exceed the minimum federal and state standards of conduct, if they choose to do so, just as states have the right to exceed federal minimums.

The basic right to exceed standards set at higher levels of government seems obvious when we relate it to standards of behavior among people within families. For example, it is generally conceded that parents do not have the right to physically abuse or willfully endanger the health or life of their children, although some may disagree with specific child welfare laws. But surely, no one would argue that parents do not have the right to treat their children better than the law requires. Surely, no one would suggest that parents must consult a team of pediatric experts before they can give their children better healthcare, nutrition, and clothing, or a better social and physical environment than is required by law. Who possibly could defend a law stating that parents could not educate their children beyond high school, unless they could produce scientific evidence that their benefit will outweigh their costs? Families obviously have a right to set their own standards of health, safety, and welfare, as long as they exceed minimum legal standards.

People in communities have the same basic rights as people in families, but community standards have to be defined and enforced by laws rather than social norms and values. There are simply too many people involved to resolve all matters personally. People in communities have the same basic rights as people in families in setting higher-than-minimum standards of conduct for people in their community. States likewise have the right to exceed national standards of health, safety, and public welfare.

But, what about situations where community standards have already been set, as in the right to farm? In such cases, changes in community standards would seem to represent a "taking" of existing rights, as is argued by the agricultural establishment. Such arguments would seem justified in those instances where farming practices are no more intrusive on their neighbors than when right to farm laws were initially accepted by the community. Communities still have the right to set higher standards, but they don't have the right to force previously conforming farmers to change.

Again, the family metaphor is relevant, as a "grandfather clause" is said to apply to conforming farmers. In families, grandfathers aren't necessarily required to change their ways, even if the rest of the family chooses some higher standard of conduct. But the rest of the family certainly doesn't have to limit itself to grandfather's level of behavior. Equally important, if grandfather starts misbehaving, by violating his earlier standards of conduct, the family has no obligation to accept his *new* behavior, just because his *old* behavior was "grandfathered in." For example, if grandfather starts mistreating the grandkids, he will quickly lose his honored status, even if he is doing nothing that violates state or federal laws.

So city, township, and county governments have a responsibility to conform to minimum safety, health, and environmental standards set by state and federal governments if we follow the logic of rights and responsibilities of individuals. But the people at each lower level of government have the right to choose standards that exceed those of the next higher level of government, without asking permission from some group of experts or providing scientific proof that higher standards are necessary. People in communities should always be open to expert opinions and scientific information, just as families should always be open to opinions and information. However, families don't have to ask permission to set higher standards of conduct and neither should local communities.

Following similar logic, farmers who are no more intrusive on their communities and their environment than when they were granted a "right to farm" still have that right; they have been "grandfathered in" to farming. However, this right to farm does not extend to industrial agricultural operations, such as CAFOs. Industrial agriculture is fundamentally different from the family farms to which the right to farm was meant to apply. The greater safety, health, and environmental risks of factory farming are well documented, and the documentation is readily available to all who are willing to inform themselves of the issue.

All farms *smell* and all farms have wastes, but factory farms *stink* and factory farms pollute. Smells may be unpleasant to those who are unaccustomed to them, but stink is just plain obnoxious and causes not only physical and mental discomfort but also clinical illness. All farms also create potentially harmful chemical and biological wastes, which can make their way into groundwater and streams. However, when livestock are dispersed across the countryside, on pasture or in small-scale facilities, they present little risk to human health or safety. Likewise, when crops are produced in rotations to control pest and provide fertility, risk of water contamination by agricultural chemicals are minimal. Dispersion and dilution mitigates potential pollution on real farms.

However, industrial agriculture inevitably pollutes streams and groundwater simply because they concentrate too many animals, too many antibiotics and hormones, and too many agricultural chemicals in too small a space. Cities are required to maintain waste treatment facilities, rather than allow individual septic systems. Extensive waste treatment is necessary to protect public health when too many people and too many industrial wastes are concentrated in too small a space. An industrial agricultural operation is more like a city than a farm, except it has thousands of animals rather than thousands of people and agrichemicals rather than industrial chemicals. So, existing farmers have no inherent right to become industrial farmers, unless they are willing to meet urban residential standards for use of chemicals and treatment of wastes. And, communities have every right to keep new industrial agricultural operations out of their communities, if they choose to do so.

This leaves only the argument that state and local health and environmental regulations cannot be allowed to interfere with interstate or intrastate commerce — that economic efficiency trumps public safety, health, and well-being. Again, the family analogy shows the inherent foolishness of this argument. Families have no responsibility to accept minimum state or federal standards, even when higher family standards clearly interfere with their participation in the marketplace. Families have no obligation to buy materials that they consider pornographic, even if such materials are legally for sale. Families have no obligation to sell their property to someone they consider to be unethical, even if that person is the highest bidder. Families have every right to reject any legal economic opportunity that they view as a threat to their health or well-being. And they don't have to consult an expert or provide scientific proof of harm.

Communities — counties, townships, and states — are made up of people and must be afforded rights as people. Rural people have every right to allow only ecologically sound and socially responsible farms to operate in their communities.

2005

06 | Reclaiming the Dignity of Rural America

rogs have an amazing ability to adjust to changing temperatures. If we were to place a frog in a pan of cold water and turn up the heat, it's been said the frog would adjust to the changing temperature and just sit there until the water came to a boil, which the frog certainly could not survive. However, if we placed a cold frog in a pan of hot water, the frog would immediately jump to safety. We humans are a bit like frogs. Sometimes, change comes so gradually that we don't realize what's happening to us until it is too late.

For decades, we have watched once thriving rural communities wither and die as farm families have been forced off the land by chronically depressed commodity prices and relentlessly rising production costs. We have seen farmers fight farmers over their neighbors' land because they were told they had to get bigger or get out. As farms became larger, farmers became fewer, and rural communities suffered the consequences. It takes people, not just production, to support a community, and fewer farms have meant fewer rural people.

We have watched the industries recruited to rural areas to replace lost farmers move on to other countries, where people were willing to work even harder for less money. Rural people then were forced to commute long distances to work because there were no jobs left in their hometowns. Eventually, they started buying their groceries, clothes, and gasoline at larger retailers in the larger towns or cities where they had found work. After a time, there were no local businesses left, except maybe a convenience store and a gas station. Main streets became ghost towns. But rural people are tough; they adjusted to hard times.

We have seen the once pristine rural environment plundered and polluted by industrialization. As industries left rural areas for other countries, many left behind legacies of pollution as well as unemployment. Now we see the industrialization of agriculture, with its reliance on agrichemicals and large-scale confinement animal feeding operations, fouling the remaining clean air, clear streams, and pure aquifers of rural areas. Many rural communities became so desperate for economic development they were willing to accept almost anything. A few succeeded in getting prisons, while others settled for landfills or toxic waste incinerators. The less fortunate are ending up with giant, corporately controlled, confinement animal feeding operations. But rural people are strong people; they learned to live with a little pollution.

In the meantime, we have watched the social fabric of rural communities being ripped apart as a few local people prospered at the expense of their neighbors who lived nearby or downwind and downstream from the rural "waste disposal sites." The injustice of such actions apparently violated an important rural ethic, and the resulting conflicts have worn away at the social fabric of the community. Rural people are gradually losing both their willingness and ability to do things together, and they must work together to clean up their environment and rebuild their communities. But rural people are independent; they have learned to live with growing isolation.

When we see increasing rural unemployment, poverty, and public dependency; when we see soil erosion, degraded landscapes, and pollution of air and water; when we see neighbors fighting neighbor over confinement hog operations or access to farmland; when we see rising drug use, epidemic crime, and physical abuse; we are seeing the consequences of rural areas being robbed of their most precious economic, natural, and human resources. And as parents encourage their children to seek better opportunities elsewhere, rural communities are losing their most precious resource — their next generation. In spite of their tremendous resilience, we are seeing rural people being robbed of their dignity.

Like frogs in a pan of hot water, the abuses have increased gradually, and the people have been able to adjust to the pain. There is nothing wrong with being tough, strong, or independent; these are all admirable traits. But there is nothing right about enduring the destruction of your community, your economy, and your way of life, just because you are able to endure it. If we keep turning up the heat, eventually the water will become hot enough to kill even the most enduring of frogs. If we keep polluting rural places and exploiting rural people, eventually it will kill even the most enduring of rural communities. If we don't turn off the heat soon, it may be too late.

Perhaps, some rural people don't think they deserve anything better. Some people are proud of being humble. But I think most rural people probably just don't believe there is much they can do about the situation, so they might as well learn to live with it. They have lived with the economic, social, and ecological abuse of rural America for so long that they have just come to accept it as their unfortunate lot in life as if it were inevitable.

I can still recall the 1950s and 1960s when many African-Americans didn't seem to think they deserved anything better; perhaps some were even proud of being humble. Many more, however, probably didn't think there was anything they could do about their situation. After all, they had been discriminated against for more than 200 years. They had learned to be tough, strong, and independent; that was the only way they could survive. Racism had always been a part of human culture; many just accepted it as inevitable.

But some African-Americans simply were not willing to endure the discrimination any longer. Perhaps they would never be accepted as equals by some people, but they were determined to reclaim their dignity and self-respect, even if they lost their lives in the process. Even if they couldn't prevent others from being racist, they had a right to protect themselves from the racial abuse. People have never had the right to exploit other people, regardless of whether the people exploited are of a different race or live in a different place. If we accept anything less, we diminish our own dignity and self-respect.

When Martin Luther King, Jr. first appeared in an all-white courtroom, he said the most difficult thing he had to do was to convince himself he actually had the right to be there. He had been discriminated against for so long he had almost forgotten that he had a right to be treated as well as anyone else. Like Rev. King, I suspect many rural people today don't feel they have a right to challenge the economically and politically powerful of our society. After all, they have been mistreated by such people for so long and have never been able to do anything about it. Some probably don't feel they have a right to demand very much from their public institutions because they have never gotten much in the past. They don't expect their government to protect them from exploitation because elected officials have been subsidizing the exploitation of rural areas for decades, in the name of economic development. Many rural people probably think it is useless to challenge economic interests because corporate profits have always been given priority over people, particularly over rural people.

Rural people have the same rights as anyone else. However, they will have to demand those rights if they expect to get them. Today, the right of rural residents to protect their health through local ordinances is being threatened, even though that right has been consistently upheld by the courts. The right to protect local natural resources from pollution and extraction and to protect local businesses from corporate domination and devastation may be even more difficult to secure. Corporate farming laws passed by referendums of the people of South Dakota and Nebraska have been recently overruled by the federal courts as violations of the Commerce Clause of the Constitution.

The Commerce Clause, however, simply states that the United States Congress shall have power . . . "To regulate Commerce with foreign Nations, and among the several States, and with the Indian Tribes." The courts have ruled that state and local governments can't do anything that interferes with interstate commerce only because the right to regulate interstate commerce is reserved for the United States Congress.

The U.S. Congress has the power to approve state laws prohibiting corporate ownership of farmland or corporate participation in farming if it chooses to do so. Or, Congress could simply pass a law stating that if the greater public interest is served by restricting corporate business activities in a specific local political jurisdiction, any resulting constraints on trade are both justified and legal. Congress could give rural people the right to protect their local economies from domination by the giant corporations, domination which clearly eliminates effective local competition, and thus, conflicts with public interests. Congress has the power to protect rural areas from exploitation; they are just unwilling to use it. Congress didn't pass the civil rights legislation of the 1960s until they were forced to do so. Likewise, Congress will likely do nothing to protect rural communities until rural people demand their basic rights of self-defense and self-reliance through local control.

There are better ways to farm than industrial farming, but these better ways will not become commonplace until rural people break the grip of corporate agribusiness. There are better economic opportunities for rural communities than being industrial waste dumps for society, but they must first break the economic grip of outside corporate domination. In spite of all the abuse, rural people are still tough, strong, and independent. While some may resent anyone else saying it, rural people only need to reclaim their dignity.

2006

SUSTAINING PEOPLE

07 | Hope for the Future of Farming

*T*here is hope for the future of farming. This hope does not suggest that things are going well for farmers, but rather that farmers have the ability to continue working for a better way of life, in spite of growing difficulties. To quote Vaclav Havel, writer, reformer, and president of the Czech Republic:

"Hope is not the same as joy when things are going well, or willingness to invest in enterprises that are obviously headed for early success, but rather an ability to work for something to succeed."

Things are not going well in agriculture. In fact, farming is in crisis. People will continue to eat, and someone will continue to produce their food. But farming, as we have known it, almost certainly is coming to an end. Agriculture is becoming increasingly industrialized — specialized and standardized with decision-making centralized among a hand-full of large agribusiness corporations. As farms continue to become larger in size, fewer in number, and increasingly under corporate control, at some point farming is no longer farming but becomes agribusiness.

So what's the difference between a farm and an agribusiness? First, farmers work with nature. Farmers recognize that the laws of nature must prevail over the laws of "man." They attempt to tip the ecological balance to favor humans over other species, but still work *with* nature. Farmers depend on unpredictable weather and work with living systems that they can never expect to completely control. Farming carries with it a set of beliefs, behaviors, and customs that distinguishes it from any other occupation. Farming is as much a way of life as a way to make a living. A farm is a good place to raise a family, and farming is a good way to be a part of a community. The benefits of farming are not solely, or even predominantly, economic in nature. It's the "culture" part of agriculture that makes a farm a farm and not an agribusiness. And the culture part of agriculture is being systematically removed through the process of industrialization.

The agricultural establishment tries to deny the existence of a crisis. They say the demise of independent family farms is a sign of technological and economic progress. The experts enjoin family farmers to prepare for a place in the corporate contract labor pool as if this was their only option. The census definition of a farm has even been changed so as to hide the precipitous decline in numbers of true farmers. In spite of the tinkering, the 1997 Census of Agriculture showed a 9 percent drop in those who consider farming their primary occupation between 1992 and 1997. The true American farm continues to disappear at an alarming rate.

Crisis is chronic in agriculture, but the current crisis is different. This crisis is not just a matter of farms continuing to become larger and fewer, instead it is a matter of completing the transformation of agriculture into an industry.

With corporations firmly in control of the economic system, and seemingly in control of the political system as well, where is the hope for farming in the future? How can farming families hope to compete with the giant agribusiness firms? How can people who are committed to stewardship compete with corporations that have no choice but to exploit nature? How can people who are committed to being good neighbors and responsible members of society compete with corporations that have no choice but to exploit other people? Where is the hope for the future of farming?

The hope for the future of farming is found in those farmers who are committed to rediscovering ways to farm that make sense, regardless of how it all turns out. Hope arises from their conviction that real farming is the only right thing to do and from their commitment to finding ways to continue doing it.

"Hope is definitely not the same thing as optimism. It's not the conviction that something will turn out well, but the certainty that something makes sense, regardless of how it turns out."

Hope for the future is in farming, not in agribusiness. This does not mean that farmers should go back to technologies and methods of the past although some may have merit for the future. Instead, hope is found in technologies and methods that respect the fundamental nature of farming and that keep the culture in agriculture, regardless of whether they are old or new. Certainly, farming in the future must yield an acceptable economic return to farmers. But an acceptable economic return is not the same thing as maximum profits and growth. Farmers of the future must regain the realization of value that results from relationships among people — within families, communities, and nations. Farmers of the future must regain the realization of value that results from living an ethical and moral life — from being good stewards or caretakers of nature and of human culture. These are things that make sense regardless of how they turn out — they are the right things to do. In these things, there is hope.

In reality, there is more reason to believe in the future of farming than in agribusiness. Agriculture has been around for centuries, while agribusiness is less than sixty years old. It's only in the past half century or so that we have allowed the economics of individual self-interest to dominate, degrade, and ultimately destroy the ethical and social values arising from farming. Farmers have been coerced, bribed, and brainwashed into believing that the only thing that really matters, or at least the thing that matters more than anything else, is the economic bottom line. The hope for the future is that farmers are beginning to realize that their blind pursuit of profits is in fact the root cause of their financial failure.

The greatest source of hope for the future is among farmers who are seeking and finding new ways to farm. They may claim the label of organic, low-input, alternative, biodynamic, holistic, permaculture, practical farmers, or just plain farmer. But they are all trying to build farming systems that are ecologically sound, economically viable, and socially responsible. They are pursuing a higher self-interest — to satisfy the personal, interpersonal, and ethical self. They realize that quality of life is a product of harmony among the economic, social, and spiritual dimensions of their lives. They refuse to exploit other people or exploit the natural environment for short run personal gain. They are building an agriculture that is sustainable over the long run, not just profitable for today. These *new American farmers* are the hope for the future of farming.

"It is this hope, above all, that gives us strength to live and to continually try new things, even in conditions that otherwise seem hopeless."

Hope gives these farmers the strength to continually try new ways of farming, even though they are working against seemingly insurmountable odds. They are the explorers, the pioneers on the new frontier of farming in America. They suffer frustrations, hardships, and even failures — but such is the nature of being pioneers. These people are doing something that no one really knows how to do. They get relatively little help from anyone other than each other, yet they persevere. But increasingly, these new farmers are finding ways to succeed.

While there are no blueprints for the new American farm, some fundamental principles are emerging. The new American farmers are creating new and better ways to make a living without abandoning the basic principles of farming.

These new American farmers focus on working with nature rather than against it. They utilize practices such as management intensive grazing, hoop-house hog operations, diverse crop rotations, cover crops, and intercropping. They manage their land and labor resources to harvest solar energy, to utilize the productivity of nature, and thus, are able to reduce their reliance on external purchased inputs.

These new American farmers focus on value rather than costs. They realize that each of us value things differently, as consumers, because we have different needs and different tastes and preferences. They market in the niches and increase value by more nearly meeting the individual needs of their customers. They market through farmers markets, roadside stands, subscription farming or CSAs, home delivery, or by customer pick-up at the farm. They market to people who care where their food comes from and how it is produced — locally grown, organic, humanely grown, or hormone and antibiotic free.

These new American farmers focus on what *they* can do best. They realize that we are all different as producers as well as consumers with widely diverse skills, abilities, and aptitudes. They may produce grass-fed beef, pastured pork, free range or pastured poultry, heirloom varieties of fruits and vegetables, dairy or meat goats, edible flowers, decorative gourds, or dozens of other products that many label as agricultural "alternatives."

In general, new American farmers focus on creating value through uniqueness — among consumers, among producers, and within nature. They link people with purpose and place, and by so doing, they create unique systems of meeting human needs that cannot be industrialized.

Will these new American farmers succeed? No one can say for sure, but there's no doubt that they *could* succeed. Hope is the *possibility* that something good *could* happen.

"Life is too precious to permit its devaluation by living pointlessly, emptily, without meaning, without love, and finally, without hope."

The future of human life depends on the future of farming. While that future is not assured, there is hope. Regardless of the odds of success, life is simply too precious to live without hope.

2001

Sustainable Agriculture: It's a Matter of People

ustainable agriculture is not just a passing fad. It's not going to go away. Sustaining agriculture ultimately is about sustaining people — not just agriculture. People are becoming increasingly concerned about today's agriculture — about its ability to meet the needs of people today and still leave opportunities for people in the future. People are becoming increasingly concerned about the safety and healthfulness of our food supplies as we increase our reliance on an impersonal, global food system. People are becoming increasingly concerned about the natural environment as agriculture moves into the final stages of corporate industrialization. People are beginning to realize that since corporations are not people they have no concern for farmers, for rural residents, or even for consumers, in any sense other than as markets for their products. Corporations have no heart, they have no soul; their only concerns are for profit and growth. People are becoming increasingly concerned about an agriculture that has no commitment to the well-being of people.

Sustainable agriculture became a public issue because of the concerns of people about people. Sustainable agriculture first came to national attention during the farm financial crisis of the 1980s. Farmers were caught up once again in a reoccurring squeeze between declining prices for agricultural commodities and rising prices for fertilizers, pesticides, fuel, and other farm inputs. The first USDA program was called Low Input Sustainable Agriculture, or LISA, because farmers were concerned about reducing their reliance on increasingly expensive inputs. Land Grant

Universities focused most willingly on the LI part of LISA, by helping farmers find ways to reduce their purchases of off-farm inputs. The SA part of the LISA program was supported by organic farming advocates, motivated by their concern for food safety and the environment. But the LISA program was mostly about helping financially distressed farm families — about helping people keep and care for their land.

The corporate agribusiness community reacted to LISA with outrage. How could the USDA and the Land Grant Universities even consider a program that might reduce the demand for agricultural inputs? They had worked hard to hook farmers on agricultural chemicals, and they weren't about to give up their "junkies" or their "dealers" without a fight. So, agribusiness and their industrial agriculture allies set about to discredit and destroy the LISA program. They used everything from making jokes about the name, to raising the specter of mass starvation, to phony "research plots" using "no fertility or pest management" to represent LISA farming systems. It was a disgraceful strategy, but it worked. USDA abandoned the LISA program and shifted the emphasis from reducing inputs to natural resource management through a new Sustainable Agriculture Research and Education (SARE) program.

SARE seemed less a threat to agribusiness than did LISA but it still met with great resistance from the agricultural establishment. The resistance was more passive than before but no less aggressive. The first reaction was to cry foul because agriculture was being singled out as a polluter, even though other industries had been "under the EPA hammer" for nearly two decades. The next strategy was for agribusiness to appear to stand by the side of farmers as trusted stewards of the natural environment, but only so long as the defense included farmers' continued use of commercial fertilizers and pesticides. Next, they promoted "wise use" of inputs by peddling costly, high-tech precision farming systems that often as not called for more, rather than fewer, inputs. Finally, agribusiness started capitalizing on environmental concerns in their marketing schemes, peddling first more costly high-tech inputs, and then biotechnology, as a means of protecting the natural environment.

The agricultural establishment has not, and will not, embrace the social dimension of agricultural sustainability. A sustainable agriculture must sustain people — not just people as consumers, but people as farmers, rural residents, and members of a civil society. Ultimately, a society will not sustain an agricultural system that will not sustain people — people as producers and citizens as well as consumers. We need look only to the collective farming systems of the former Soviet Union for a prime example. A socially irresponsible agriculture can do great harm to society as a centrally planned agriculture did to the Soviet Union. A corporate dominated, vertically integrated agriculture, which looms over the American horizon, is a centrally planned agriculture — no different in concept from a communist economy. It is not a socially responsible system and thus quite simply is not sustainable.

Sustainable agriculture research and educational programs are being challenged today as never before. Funding for the USDA SARE program is challenged each budget year and stays alive only through the diligent efforts of politically active non-profit organizations and grass roots support groups. So far, SARE appears to be holding its own. However, in recent years, several major Land Grant Universities have dropped their sustainable agriculture programs and others have integrated them into other less controversial program areas.

Public universities have become increasingly reliant on corporations to fund their research programs. In most cases, this means increasing emphasis on biotechnology. Biotechnology has not and will not be embraced by the sustainable agriculture movement. Biotechnology is a tool designed to manipulate and dominate nature, and sustainability ultimately will require that we instead farm in harmony with nature. The universities quite simply are not willing to jeopardize their chances for multimillion-dollar corporate funded biotech projects by protecting a few-thousand-dollar publicly funded sustainable agriculture programs.

Perhaps even more important, public universities have lost faith in their ability to be of significant benefit to people — at least to people directly. They argue that they serve the public through their work with corporations — that scientific discoveries must be "commercialized" before the science becomes of use to the public. They seem to have forgotten that discoveries can be commercialized through individual decision-makers, through farmers and other independent business people, not just through corporations. It's just easier and more comfortable for universities to work with a large agribusiness than to work with a similarly large group of individual farmers or citizens.

The universities seem to have forgotten that tax dollars are not only to be used to support research that benefits the public, but to support only research "that the private sector will not adequately support." Agricultural colleges were publicly funded because farmers were too small to do their own research, and agricultural research had clear public benefits. The giant agribusiness corporations are perfectly capable of funding their own research — all of it. In addition, these corporations don't operate in competitive markets. Thus, most of the benefits will end up as corporate profits, not lower prices for consumers or higher prices for farmers. Why should the taxpayer be footing any part of the bill?

As public institutions worked less directly with people, for the direct good of people, they have lost the support of people, and their public funding has declined. Taxpayers were getting fewer benefits, and ultimately, they refused to pay for benefits they weren't getting. They asked their legislators to hold the line or to cut funding for public research and education. So now, the universities are turning to corporate support because of lagging public support, and the public is getting even fewer benefits for their tax dollars. It's a vicious circle from which there is no easy way out.

Sustainable agriculture will never be funded, or even tolerated, by agribusiness because it is fundamentally about reducing reliance on off-farm inputs, protecting the natural environment, and empowering people to free themselves from corporate domination. Sustainable agriculture will never be funded, or even tolerated, by large farm commodity groups because it promotes diversification rather than specialization. Sustainable agriculture is about people rather than production. If sustainable agriculture research and education is to be funded, it will have to be funded publicly, by the people.

Sustainable agriculture promotes smaller, more-diversified family farms because of its focus on people. It seeks greater economic rewards to farmers, rather than more profits for input suppliers. It seeks ways to farm in harmony with nature, rather than to conquer nature. And it seeks to support farming as a quality way of life, as well as a way to make a living. If agriculture is to be sustainable, we must have enough farmers to sustain the productivity and ecological health of the land. Thus, sustainability will require more, rather than fewer, farmers — more who understand their particular parcel of land, who know how to take care of it, who are motivated to care for it, and who have the time and money to care for it well, more farmers who "love the land." And, each farmer can "love" only so much land.

Sustainable agriculture promotes greater concern among people — people making conscious, purposeful decisions for the common good rather than relying on the impersonal forces of the marketplace. The *invisible hand* of capitalist economics that is supposed to transform individual greed into the common good has been mangled in the machinery of corporate consolidation. The markets will not ensure that the hungry will be fed. The markets will not ensure that people willing to work will have an opportunity to work. The markets will not ensure that future generations will have adequate resources to meet their needs for food, clothing, and shelter. The only way to ensure that the needs of the present and future are met is to make conscious, purposeful decisions to care for the natural environment and to care for other people.

This is the mandate of sustainable agriculture: to care about people of this generation and people of all generations to come. It's a mandate that too few are yet willing to accept, but a mandate that ultimately cannot be denied. Sustainable agriculture must be about sustaining people through agriculture, not just sustaining agriculture.

2000

09 | Farming for Quality of Life

*T*alk with any farmer about why he or she is farming, and they will probably mention that they would like to make some money. Making money may not be at the top of their list, particularly for smaller, part-time farmers, but it will probably be somewhere in their top ten. Yet many small farmers continue to farm, even though they lose money year after year, because there are sound, logical reasons for farming other than making money.

According to USDA statistics, only 67 percent of small, "limited resource" farms and 63 percent of small, "lifestyle" farms reported positive net-cash incomes from farming in 2004. For "primary occupation" small farmers (with less than $100,000 annual sales), only 69 percent reported positive net-cash incomes. For these three USDA small farm groups combined, only 65 percent made any money farming. These latest detailed financial figures were similar to estimates for earlier years and there's no reason to believe that the situation has improved much since then.

Some people look at such statistics and conclude that small farmers aren't serious about farming. For most of these small farmers, farming must be a hobby, they say, a serious farmer would either find a way to make money or get out. I suspect that every one of these small farmers would rather make a profit than take a loss. But I suspect also that they haven't gotten out of farming because making money wasn't the most important reason they were farming in the first place. And for most, farming is not a hobby; it's a serious business. Many of these farmers are achieving what's most important to many small farmers, and that isn't making money.

A lot of small farms are "quality of life" farms — their primary purpose is to contribute to the quality of life of a farm family in ways other than economic. Typically, one or more members of the family on such farms has an off-farm job to provide the family with necessary "cash" income. This allows their farming operation to focus on the other aspects of a desirable quality of life. It would cost a lot of money for people living in cities to buy the quality of life benefits that are an inherent part of a good family farm. And other quality of life benefits of farming are truly "priceless."

Ask farm families why they farm, and many will mention that they like the open spaces, fresh air, scenic landscapes, and the opportunity to live in a natural setting. How much money does a person have to earn in a city to live in a scenic, natural environment with fresh air and open spaces? Even small farms provide families very large "residential lots," averaging more than 200 acres. How much money does a person have to earn in a city to "buy" this much open space, personal freedom, and privacy?

Ask farm families why they farm, and many will mention that a farm is a good place to raise a family. A good farm is a place that nurtures life — plants and animals — and the lives of children can be nurtured by growing up on a farm. Farm families also can have more influence on their children because families have opportunities to spend more quality time together — work and family life happens at the same place. Children who grow up knowing they are valued, productive participants in the work of the family would logically seem more likely to grow up with a healthy sense of self-worth. How much money does a family have to earn in a city to ensure high quality learning opportunities for their children, to create opportunities for the family to grow together, to give their children opportunities to build self-esteem? How much time and money is spent by families in cities just to keep the children "occupied" with "non-destructive" activities? The things that build strong families just come naturally in day-to-day life on a good family farm.

Ask farm families why they farm, and many will mention that they like being part of a farming community. Farming communities may not be as close-knit as they were back in the days when farmers shared work and when the social life of farm families was pretty much limited to community activities. However, many farming communities are still places where everyone knows just about everyone else, and everybody has an opportunity to pursue whatever community roles they choose to pursue. How much time and money does a person in a city have to spend to develop and maintain a social network of friends? How much time and money does a person in a city have to spend to develop name recognition and credibility if they decide to take on a leadership role in their "community?" Farmers just naturally find a place to belong in communities with other farming families.

On a family farm, the open spaces, the place to raise a family, and the community, all come as part of farming. You don't have to pay extra for the extra space because you need the same space for the farm. You don't have to pay extra for a place to raise a family because the place you raise the family is the farm. And you don't have to pay extra to be a part of a farming community because you become a part of it when you decide to live there and farm. These benefits are valuable, but you don't have to pay anything extra for them; they are just part of the quality of life that comes with farming.

As a bonus, the costs of many such quality of life benefits are considered as farming costs. The cost of owning farmland is a farming cost although the farm provides a place to live. Many food costs are also farm costs, such as some of the costs of a vegetable garden and animals for meat, eggs, or milk. Some family transportation costs are farm costs — every farm needs a pickup truck. Many recreation costs, such as maintaining wildlife habitat for hunting and fishing, all-terrain vehicles for work and play, a stable for riding horses, and pets that "work" on the farm are also farm costs. To the extent that they also contribute to the farm business, things that contribute to a desirable quality of life on a farm are legitimate costs of farming.

What difference does this make whether something is a farm cost or family cost? If something is a business cost, it can be deducted from farm income, reducing farm income for accounting and tax purposes. Expenses of a purely personal nature are not deductible. So, for each dollar spent for personal expense, a person has to earn anywhere from $1.20 to $1.45, depending on their federal and state income tax brackets. Farmers only have to earn a dollar to spend a dollar on legitimate farm expenses, including those that create valuable personal benefits. And every dollar "lost" on the farm may save from $0.20 to $0.45 in reduced taxes on off-farm income.

Many small farms that report "negative" net incomes still may be providing very valuable economic benefits to farm families. In fact, it's conceivable that the costs of providing the same quality of life benefits that occur on many small family farms might require $30,000 to $50,000 in off-farm income. The costs of such things as an acreage in an upscale gated community, enhanced private educational and recreational experiences for children, involvement in civic affairs, maintaining social relationships, and membership in a sport's club don't come cheap. So, a farm that just "breaks even" might be contributing as much to the quality of life of the family as a job that pays $30,000 to $50,000 in town.

Many people who earn $30,000, $50,000, and/or even much more from their jobs in town are able to do little more than pay the cost of living of their families — the cost of their quality of life. And many city families need more than one income, and sometimes more than one job per person, just to make ends meet. A farm that just breaks even is still making ends meet. Off-farm employment may be necessary only because some things that contribute to a desirable quality of life can't be produced on the farm, and thus require a cash income.

Some other aspects of life on a farm are simply "priceless." Our quality of life simply cannot be measured by our income or wealth — although economic rewards are a part of it. Our quality of life also depends on the quality of our relationships with other people. And our quality of life depends on whether we find purpose and meaning in the things that we do — whether we are living and working according to our moral and ethical principles. We can't buy a life of quality; we must live it. And the most important dimensions of our quality of life are truly "priceless."

For many farm families, farming is the means by which they build positive relationships within their families and communities, and by which they accept their responsibilities for helping build a better society. For many farm families, being good stewards of the land, caring for the land for the benefit of current and future generations, gives purpose and meaning to their lives. These "quality of life farmers" are sustainable farmers — they are economically viable, ecologically sound, and socially responsible farmers. And many of these farmers live and work on small family farms. For these farm families, and for society as a whole, the benefits of living and working on a "quality of life" farm are truly "priceless."

2001

10 | Why Do Small Farmers Farm?

A lot of time and mental energy has been spent by people attempting to classify farms. What is a small farm, a family farm, a corporate farm, and so on? But the more important question may be, "Why do people farm?" Questions of whether a farm is large or small, a family farm or a farm business, or controlled by an individual or corporation simply reflect different reasons for farming. If we classified farms by "why farmers farm," I suggest we would find three different types of farms: commercial farms, lifestyle farms, and stewardship farms.

The USDA currently defines farms with less than $50,000 annual sales as being "noncommercial," suggesting that their purpose is something other than making money. USDA's "Residence/lifestyle" farms and "retirement" farms are defined as farms with operators who have principal occupations other than farming, implying the farm is mainly a place to live. USDA's criteria for "limited resource" farms provide little insight into why these farmers are farming. Farms with sales over $50,000, where farming is the "primary occupation," and resources are not limited, are presumed, by default, to be a "commercial farm" — farms intended to generate significant income for the farm operator. While we may question the specific criteria, USDA's categories of farms at least give some recognition to the fact that one's reasons for farming are relevant.

To USDA's "commercial" and "lifestyle" farms, I would add a third farm type: a "stewardship" farm. The principal purpose of a stewardship farm is to conserve and care for the land and other natural resources of the farm.

The most obvious examples of stewardship farms today are those in the Conservation Reserve Program. In this case, the government is providing a stewardship incentive. But I believe there are thousands of farmers who own and manage farmland for the primary purpose of stewardship, who are not receiving government incentives. Of course, many of these land-owners expect the value of land to increase enough to offset property taxes and other costs, so they are not necessarily making economic sacrifices. But stewardship farmers may neither live on the land nor attempt to make money from farming.

The principal purpose of a stewardship farm is to pass the land on to the next generation in as good a condition, or better, than when it was passed to this generation. The principal purpose of a commercial farm is to generate economic returns — regardless of whether it is controlled by a family or a corporation. The principal purpose of a lifestyle farm is to provide a good place to live — regardless of whether the farm operator is employed elsewhere or is retired.

USDA's classifications of farms reflect an implicit assumption that the primary purpose of farming in the U.S. is commercial — that a real farm is a "farm business." They define a farm with less than $50,000 in annual sales as noncommercial because they assume it would be difficult to gener-ate a significant amount of net farm income on a farm this small. Net farm incomes average only about 15–17 percent of total sales on farms produc-ing basic agricultural commodities, such as corn, wheat, soybeans, hogs, cattle, cotton, wholesale vegetables, fruits, and berries using *conventional* farming methods. Thus, $50,000 in gross sales would only generate about $8,000 in net farm income. When the National Commission on Small Farms included farms with up to $250,000 in their definition of *small* farms, the implicit conclusion was that since farms of this size usually gen-erate around $40,000 in net farm income, they are really not very big.

Likewise, when using acres as a measure of size, the justification gener-ally comes back to the question of "how big a farm does it take to generate a significant amount of net farm income?" Invariably, the answer assumes that farms produce basic farm commodities using conventional methods of production and marketing. Over the decades, more and more land and sales of commodities have been required to generate enough income to support a farm family. Thus, farms have had to become larger and larger over the years and decades just to maintain an acceptable level of living for farm owners and operators.

The relationship between farm size and stewardship is quite different. No one states the nature of this relationship more eloquently than Wendell Berry in his book, *What Are People For?* "If the land is to be used well, the people who use it must know it well, must be highly motivated to use it well, must know how to use it well, must have time to use it well, and must be able to afford to use it well." He goes on to write, "Farming by the measure of nature, which is to say the nature of the particular place, means that farmers must tend farms that they know and love, farms small enough to know and love, using tools and methods they know and love, in the company of neighbors they know and love."

Obviously, a landowner could set a large tract of land aside as a natural area, and in so doing, be a good steward of a very large farm. But such a farm or ranch would not generate much income or produce much of economic benefit to society. If land is to generate income and create a good place for people to live, the land must be used but used well. And thus, most farms and ranches must be *smaller* than they are today. The emphasis on the commercial purpose of farming has encouraged, essentially forced, most farms to become so large that farmers can no longer use the land well. Each farmer can only truly know and love so much land.

The relationship between farm size and farm lifestyle is similar to that of size and stewardship. With respect to the physical environment — open space, fresh air, scenic landscapes — residence farms may be any size, and up to a point, larger may seem to be better. Beyond some point, however, farms or ranches get larger at the expense of their neighbors and their communities, regardless of whether the motive for expansion is commercial or residential. And the quality of the farmer or rancher's relationships with his or her neighbors ultimately affects the quality of the *place* where they live.

Wendell Berry's words apply, just as accurately, to relationships among rural people as among farmers and the land. If our rural communities are to remain healthy, desirable places to live, they must preserve the health and productivity of people, their physical, emotional, and spiritual well-being; the people, that is, must be treated well. A further requirement is that if people are to treat each other well, they must know each other well, must be motivated to treat each other well, must have time to treat each other well, and must be able to afford to treat each other well. If our rural communities are to remain good places to live, we must have communities of people who love each other. And we cannot have communities of people who love each other if some feel that they must drive others away so they can buy more land.

This brings us to a fourth purpose for farming, farming for sustainability. Sustainability requires that farmers be motivated by the purposes of economic viability (commercial), ecological integrity (stewardship), and social responsibility (lifestyle). If farmers or ranchers focus on any one of the three, without giving conscious purposeful consideration of the other two, they inevitably threaten the sustainability of their farming operations. Farms or ranches that focus on economic viability, meaning commercial farms, eventually will become too large to use the land well and inevitably will degrade their relationships with their neighbors. Similarly, farms that focus only on individual lifestyle — excluding concern for neighbors, productivity, or the natural environment — may threaten sustainability. And farms or ranches that focus solely on stewardship do nothing to support healthy community relationships or to provide for the food and fiber or employment needs of people. In all three cases, by focusing on a single purpose, they threaten sustainability. Largeness is not the cause of the lack of sustainability of a farm, but instead, is a symptom of a narrow focus on a single purpose of farming — typically, on commercial farming.

Of course, farms and ranches can also be too small to be sustainable, meaning they can't generate enough income, can't take care of the land, nor provide a good place to live. But farmers who rely on *alternative* farming methods — reduce input costs, market in the niches, build relationships, and so on — can generate more net income with fewer acres of land and fewer dollars invested. An intensively managed sustainable farm may generate fifty cents, or more, in net farm income for each dollar of sales. Thus, a farm with $100,000 in sales can generate $50,000 in net farm income, and a farm classified by USDA as noncommercial may add $25,000 or more to farm household income. Unlike farms that are too large, farms that are too small do relatively little harm to the economy, the environment, or to the community, and thus, to the overall sustainability of agriculture.

The fundamental purpose of a sustainable farm or ranch is to create a desirable quality of life. Quality of life has economic (commercial), ecological (stewardship), and social (lifestyle) dimensions. A desirable quality of life requires balance and harmony among the personal (economic), ethical (ecological), and relational (social) dimensions of life. It's simply easier to balance the commercial, stewardship, and lifestyle purposes for farming on a small farm. Why do many small farmers farm for sustainability? They are farming for quality of life.

2003

11 | Farming with Purpose & Principles

*D*uring the farm financial crisis of the 1980s, I recall being unable to understand why many farmers committed suicide when confronted with the inevitable loss of their farms. I now believe that they had lost their sense of purpose in life. They thought they were meant to be farmers, and if they could no longer farm, they could see no reason for living. They were right, at least in a sense; if our life has no purpose, it makes no difference whether we are living or dead. If we aren't meant to do anything in particular, it doesn't matter what we do or don't do. Had these farmers thought more rationally about their purpose in life, perhaps they would have lived to fulfill it.

Over the years, I have met many farmers, particularly those on small farms, who truly believe they were meant to be farmers. Farming to them is not just a means of making money so they can buy things that will make them happy; farming is the thing that makes them happy. They feel good when they are able to take care of their land. They feel good when they are able to be a good neighbor. Farming today is a business, and farmers must make money to continue farming. Still, many farmers today don't farm to make money; they make money so they can farm. Their purpose in life is to be a farmer.

The big question for farmers and for the rest of us is, "How can we find our purpose in life?" Like most important questions in life, this one doesn't have a simple answer. The best answer I have is, "If we live by true principles, we will be guided toward our purpose." It simply doesn't make sense that we would be given a purpose that would require us to violate the important principles of life. But this still leaves us with the task of discovering life's true principles.

First, principles are different from values. Different people may have very different values, but the important principles of life are true for everyone. Principles are defined by our "common sense" of the nature of things — the sense that we share in common with others. In the 1700s, this common sense was referred to as *natural law*, as when the Founding Fathers of the United States declared certain "truths to be self evident" including the inalienable rights of all to "life, liberty, and the pursuit of happiness." Principles are self-evident — common sense.

The search for purpose is something like a scientific experiment; we first propose or hypothesize our purpose, such as, "I am meant to be a farmer." We then test our proposition or hypothesis by pursuing our proposed purpose guided by the principles relevant to that purpose. For example, if we hypothesize that our purpose is farming, and if we are able to farm without violating any of the important principles of farming, we probably were meant to be a farmer.

When we find our purpose in life, we also will find happiness, since happiness is the ultimate purpose of all human endeavors. *Making money* is not a purpose for living. Money is always a means of acquiring something else — something that will make us happy. So in finding our purpose, we need to focus on what would actually make us happy, not just making money. If we are meant to be wealthy, we won't have to exploit anyone or anything in the process of acquiring wealth; we will do principled things with our wealth, and those things will make us happy. Most of us obviously were not meant to be wealthy although I believe we were all meant to be happy.

The principles most relevant to any particular purpose depend upon the basic nature of the purpose. A farm is a living system which relies on the life within the soil and life upon the soil, including plants, animals, and people. All living systems, including organisms and organizations, function according to a set of common principles, which include holism, diversity, and interdependence.

The whole of a farm is more than a simple collection of individual activities or enterprises; its essence also depends upon the relationships among those activities and enterprises. When the crops within a rotation are changed, or the sequence of crops in a rotation is changed, the farming system as a whole is changed. Crop rotations are effective in maintaining soil fertility or managing pests only when the crops used in rotations are fundamentally different or diverse. Some fix nitrogen, some break pest cycles, some control erosion, and some make money.

When activity or enterprises are integrated so as to compliment each other, their relationships are interdependent or mutually beneficial. The whole is something more than the sum of its parts. The health and regenerative capacity of any living system depends upon interdependent relationships among its diverse components within its inseparable whole. A farm that is managed according to these basic principles is capable of maintaining its productivity indefinitely.

Farming is an intentional activity, carried out with intent of meeting the needs of people, as consumers and producers of food and as members of society. The physical or material needs of people are met through productivity, but the social needs of people depend upon relationships. If a particular way of farming creates continual conflicts within families, among neighbors, and between different groups within society, it is not a principled way to farm, no matter how profitable it may seem. All human relationships depend on a common set of core principles, which include trust, caring, and courage.

Farmers who expect to maintain good relationships with their customers and neighbors must be honest and truthful in their communications, fair and equitable in their dealings, and dependable and responsible in their commitments. Over time, such farmers will build a reputation of trustworthiness and will find that many customers and political allies place a high value on being able to relate to and deal with someone they know they can trust. At times, however, farmers must be willing to be more than fair and do more than their share if they are to sustain their relationships. Everyone makes mistakes now and then, and everyone experiences occasional misfortunes. Farmers must be respectful and compassionate in their relationships with customers and neighbors, doing for others as they would have others to do for them. They must be caring as well as trustworthy.

It also takes courage to trust and to care. Trusting and caring are of little real value unless they result in actions. Many farmers have been told they must be independent and competitive if they are to succeed. It takes courage to reject the conventional wisdom of success through independence and to embrace the common sense of happiness through relationships.

If a farm is to be financially viable, it must function according to the fundamental principles of economics, which include value, productivity, and sovereignty. Economic value is determined by scarcity. To prosper economically, farmers must be willing to produce things that are scarce

— things their customers cannot readily find elsewhere at lower costs. Today, there is a scarcity of ecological and social integrity, as well as high quality foods. Productivity results from the use of resources — land, labor, management, and creativity — to produce things that people value. Farmers on small farms must be able to combine their resources more creatively since they have fewer resources to combine. Economic value and productivity arise from wise choices. Sovereignty is the freedom to choose. Farmers that give up their sovereignty, through large debts or contractual commitments, sacrifice their ability to create productivity. Farmers need not cherish the principles of economics, but they must respect them.

Finally, the economic, social, and ecological principles of farming must function in harmony. Economic and ecological relationships must be honest, fair, responsible, respectful, and compassionate. The economic and social aspects of a farm must reflect holism, diversity, and interdependence. And a farm's ecological and social relationships must produce things of value without sacrificing individual sovereignty. Farming systems simply cannot continue to function with conflicting principles. If a farmer is truly pursuing his or her purpose in life, he or she will never be forced to compromise the ecological, social, or economic principles of farming.

Unfortunately, many farmers seem to feel that they must compromise the principles of ecological stewardship and personal relationships in order to make their farms economically viable. However, if farming is their purpose in life, they will not have to compromise their fundamental principles of farming to pursue it. Farmers who view a farm as strictly a business obviously don't see the relevance of the ecological or social principles of farming. But it simply doesn't make sense that a farmer would have to violate principles that they know to be relevant and important in order to pursue their purpose.

The farmers who committed suicide during the 1980s simply didn't understand that they would not have been given a purpose that they were fundamentally incapable of continuing to pursue. The financial failures of their farms were either a reflection of violations of the principles of farming or were an indication that farming no longer served their purpose. With a better understanding of purpose, their decisions still would not have been easy, but suicide would not have been considered a logical alternative. The means by which we fulfill our purpose in life necessarily changes with age and changing circumstances in life. If farming is making you miserable, you probably need to change the way you farm or look elsewhere for your purpose. If farming makes you happy, you are probably meant to be a farmer.

2006

SUSTAINING AGRICULTURE

12 | Organic Farming & Sustainable Agriculture

*M*ention *sustainable agriculture* and many people will think you are talking about organic farming. Some organic farmers will agree. Some farmers think organic farming is the only way of farming that can sustain agricultural production over the long run. They may be right. No one knows for sure whether any particular system of farming is or is not sustainable. However, most people involved with the sustainable agriculture issue see organic farming and sustainable agriculture as two related, but distinctly different, concepts.

There are many different definitions of sustainable agriculture. However, there is growing consensus that a sustainable agriculture must be capable of maintaining its productivity and usefulness to society over the long run. To do this, it must be ecologically sound, economically viable, and socially responsible.

Sustainable systems must be capable of providing for the food and fiber needs of society at a reasonable cost and must provide an acceptable level of living for farmers. Farming systems that fail in these respects, such as the communist collective farms of Eastern Europe, are neither politically nor financially sustainable over time. Sustainable systems must also conserve their natural resource base and protect their environment. Systems that use up or degrade their resource base lose their ability to produce and, thus, are not sustainable. Likewise, farming practices that poison the people's water or air in the process of producing their food will not sustain people and, thus, will not be sustained by people. In general, a sustainable agriculture must make a positive contribution to the overall quality of life of farmers, other rural residents, and of society as a whole.

Are organic farming systems sustainable? There is no general agreement on the answer to that question. Like sustainable agriculture, organic farming has a variety of definitions. Many people refer to organic farming as farming without the use of manufactured or man-made chemical inputs. Organic farmers must rely primarily on mechanical and cultural practices, such as crop rotations and cultivation to control pests. However, commercially available biological pesticides are becoming popular among many organic farmers. Organic farmers may rely on nitrogen fixing legumes, green manure crops, animal manure, and mined minerals to provide crop nutrients. However, they cannot use manufactured fertilizers. Organic farming eliminates the risks to water quality and food safety posed by commercial pesticides and fertilizers. But there are disagreements concerning whether organic farming reduces overall environmental risks and whether organic farms could provide for the food and fiber needs of society.

Agricultural scientists point out that nitrogen can leach into groundwater from organic sources, such as legume crops and animal manure, as well as from application of commercial nitrogen. In fact, commercial nitrogen may be easier to manage and thus less subject to unintentional over-application. Food chemists also point out that many of the most toxic chemicals found in foods are naturally occurring substances. They also contend that many of the manufactured chemicals are less toxic than many common food items, such as table salt.

Scientists who support organic farming counter that the human species has successfully evolved over the last hundred centuries or so with organic farming methods. Manufactured chemical inputs have been used for less than a single century of that time. Many of the chemicals now considered dangerous to human health or the environment, such as DDT, were considered to be safe for general use a few decades ago. In addition, most of the scientific data on agricultural chemicals relates to single chemicals used in isolation rather than in combinations with other chemicals as they are commonly used in agriculture.

Highly competent scientists disagree with respect to the relative risks of conventional and organic systems of production. It will take many years, if not decades, of scientific experiments to develop a preponderance of evidence in support of one side or the other.

In reality, these disagreements among scientists are much more a matter of philosophy than of science. All scientists, no matter how objective, start from a philosophical foundation of value judgments. They begin with their own assumptions regarding *how the world works* and of *the purpose of life*. These things have not been and cannot be proven by science. Scientists on both sides should recognize that their differences are philosophical rather than factual in nature and should address the scientific questions of sustainability from that perspective.

A recent study by two rural sociologists, Beus and Dunlop, explored the philosophical roots of the debate between "conventional" and "alternative" agriculture advocates. (Organic farmers tend to be near the "alternative" end of a continuum between these two views of agriculture.) Beus and Dunlop conclude that no other element of the debate is as fundamental as "how humans should relate to their environment." The two sides agree that interaction with nature is an essential aspect of farming, but they disagree on almost everything else.

Conventional agriculturalists frequently use the analogy of war in describing their relationship with the environment. They describe weeds and insects as the enemy or adversaries with which farmers must wage war to survive. Agricultural scientists seek to unlock the secrets of nature in order to bend nature to the will of humankind. They see pesticides and fertilizers as a means of defeating the enemies that subtract from our ability to reap the Earth's bounty. Use of agricultural chemicals is viewed as a forward step towards controlling the environment in ways that will accommodate greater human well-being and comfort.

Alternative agriculturalists see this kind of adversarial relationship with nature as being futile and self-defeating. They contend that humans and nature are inseparable. They view humans as part of an interrelated ecological system that includes weeds, insects, and other animal species as well as humans. Our well-being as humans is thus interrelated with the well-being of the system as a whole. They contend that scientists should seek to understand nature, not in order to conquer nature, but rather to learn to live in harmony with nature. Agricultural chemicals are seen as being potentially destructive to the natural processes of production upon which humanity must ultimately depend.

How *should* humans relate to nature? Science is fundamentally incapable of answering this question. One group thinks that we must conquer nature if humanity is to survive. The other group thinks we must learn to live in harmony with nature if humanity is to survive. In the face of conflicting philosophies, it seems prudent that science should provide as much information as possible about a range of alternatives for the future.

Sustainable agriculture embraces a range of alternative philosophies of farming. A sustainable agriculture must be ecologically sound, economically viable, and socially responsible. Any set of farming practices or methods that fails to achieve any one of these objectives will not be sustainable over time. Sustainability is a site-specific, individualistic, dynamic concept. Systems that are sustainable for one farmer or farm at one point in time may not be sustainable for another farmer or farm at another point in time. Thus, sustainability cannot be associated with any particular set of farming practices or methods. Sustainability is characteristic of the performance of individual farmers and whole-farm systems.

Some contend that sustainability must be achieved by fine-tuning conventional systems of farming. They do not believe that lower-input or organic systems of farming will ever be capable of feeding the growing world population. Others argue that sustainability will require a different model or paradigm for farming that relies less on commercial inputs and more on farm resource management. They see the input-dependent, industrial model of agricultural as being fundamentally incompatible with maintaining a healthy ecological and social environment. Advocates of organic farming believe that sustainability will require the total elimination of manufactured chemical inputs. Others propose still different models of farming as a means of achieving long-run agricultural sustainability.

The most important aspect of these various perspectives of agriculture should be their points of general agreement rather than their many minor points of disagreement. All seem to agree that the sustainability of humanity depends on the sustainability of agriculture. There also seems to be general agreement that we should look beyond the current decade or even the current generation and become concerned about the long-run survival of humanity. Disagreement about the means of achieving sustainability need not be destructive, or even counterproductive, so long as we agree to pursue the goal of a long-term sustainable agriculture.

1993

Reference: Curtis E. Beus and Riley E. Dunlop, "Conventional versus Alternative Agriculture: The Paradigmatic Roots of the Debate," Rural Sociology 55(4) 1990, 590-616.

13 Livestock in Sustainable Farming Systems

here do livestock fit into sustainable farming systems, and how do livestock producers meet the challenges of raising livestock sustainably? The answers to these questions could open up new opportunities for smaller, diversified farmers in the future.

In sustainable agriculture circles, livestock typically are viewed as a means of increasing the sustainability of crop production. Diversity is needed in crop rotations to break pest cycles and fix nitrogen from the air, thus reducing the need for commercial pesticides and fertilizers. Such rotations seem to work best in integrated crop-livestock farming systems. Grain crops, forage crops, and crop residue can be fed to livestock on the farms where they are produced and livestock manure can be returned to the fields where the crops were grown, reducing the need for commercial fertilizers. In general, livestock seem to complement sustainable systems of crop production.

Livestock also add physical and economic diversity that is not present in crop farming operations. Diversified farmers are less vulnerable to weather and market risks that can be disastrous for specialized crop producers. Livestock have been an important part of diversified farming systems of the past, and livestock enterprises are likely to be important components of modern diversified farming systems of the future.

Livestock do fit into sustainable farming systems, but the issue of sustainable agriculture presents challenges, as well as opportunities, for livestock producers. Controlling the water pollution associated with livestock wastes may prove more challenging than controlling nutrient leaching and runoff from commercial fertilizers used on crops. The energy required to produce meats, compared with direct human consumption of grain, is a common resource concern. Drug and hormone residues in meats may be at least as common as pesticide residues in fruits and vegetables. And animal welfare is a public issue of increasing social concern that could have major impacts on livestock production in the future.

The challenges for livestock producers are fairly straightforward and similar in most respects to those of crop producers. Can livestock and poultry be produced by methods that conserve natural resources, protect the natural environment, provide adequate supplies of safe and healthful foods by socially acceptable means at reasonable costs, and still provide an acceptable level of economic return for livestock producers?

Large confinement beef, poultry, and dairy operations tend to be the focus of such concerns. Water and air pollution from livestock wastes, residues of antibiotics and growth additives in meats and milk, humane treatment of animals raised in confinement, and impacts of large, corporate operations on opportunities of smaller livestock producers are all questions raised by those concerned about the sustainability of conventional livestock systems.

Large commercial livestock feeding operations are the source of most questions regarding energy use in meat and milk production. Grain-fed beef, for example, yields only a small fraction of the energy embodied in the feedstuffs consumed by cattle in the production process. Poultry and pork production are more energy efficient than beef production, but all are far less efficient than direct human consumption of grains.

However, those in the livestock industry should insist that questions of energy efficiency in meat production be addressed in the same social context as the disproportionate use of energy in the more developed countries of the world in general. Affluent societies do consume more grain-fed meats, but affluent people use more energy of all types. The inequities in energy use reflect the reality of current world economic systems, not the ethics of cattle feeding or any other particular method of energy conversion.

Most environmental questions for livestock producers also relate to large-scale confinement animal feeding operations or CAFOs. Nutrient runoff from feedlots is an obvious potential source of water pollution. But mismanagement of manure removed from cattle feedlots or confinement hog and poultry facilities can be just as important. Farmers may apply manure at such times or by methods that result in most of the nutrients being volatilized, eroded, or leached rather than used by growing plants. Or they may apply manure effectively, but still apply the same amount of fertilizer they would have used without manure, resulting in pollution from excess nutrient application.

Confinement livestock and poultry operations are also the primary users of sub-therapeutic levels of antibiotics. Such practices may result in pathogenic resistance, thus reducing the effectiveness of these antibiotics for therapeutic uses in humans. Growth hormones have also been used extensively in livestock feeding operations. The association of DES with cancer has resulted in heightened public concern regarding the use of growth hormones in general. The concern for use of growth hormones is combined with public distrust of biotechnology in the current public controversy concerning the use of a genetically engineered bovine growth hormone, rGBH, in milk.

Social questions regarding animal welfare are also most frequently associated with confinement livestock operations. To date, producers of veal and caged layer chickens have received most of the animal welfare publicity. However, the basic issues are the same for all animals produced in confinement. To what extent can the activity of animals be restricted for purposes of production or economic efficiency without violating our social values concerning humane treatment of animals?

Confinement livestock operations can put more beef, pork, and chicken on the market at a lower dollar and cent cost than can free-range operations or farmer feeders. Thus, confinement operations have been considered more economically sustainable than alternative systems of livestock production. But questions are now being raised regarding ecologic and social costs of confinement production. The answers to these questions could shift the competitive balance in favor of less grain feeding, smaller farm-based operations, or even more grass- and forage-finished livestock.

One example of how small farmers could profit from this shift may be found in the Missouri beef industry. Many of Missouri's rolling farmlands are exceptionally well suited for forage-based beef production. Much of this land already supports herds of beef and dairy cattle. However, many of Missouri's marginal crop lands could be utilized more sustainably in forage production if cattle could compete with crops in terms of productivity and profitability.

Forage-based beef production has some potentially strong positive ecological attributes of sustainability. Many forage crops are close-growing perennials which protect the soil from erosion and facilitate water infiltration. Forages also require less nonrenewable energy to establish and harvest than do most row crops. And in many cases, forages are less reliant on the commercial fertilizers and pesticides that represent environmental risks.

Forages may also be the most efficient sustainable converters of solar energy on many soil types. In fact, the greatest inherent comparative advantage of cattle may be as intermediate energy converters. Some soils and climates will not grow crops that can be utilized directly by humans. Cattle, or other ruminants, may represent the most practical means of converting such energy to a form useful to humans.

Cattle on pastures are less likely to develop diseases than are cattle in feed lots and thus, are less likely to require use of antibiotics or other drugs than feedlot cattle. Parasites, however, may be a greater problem for range cattle. Growth hormones are sometimes used in cattle on pasture but less commonly than in feedlot cattle. Raising cattle on pastures is also commonly conceded as being more humane than is confinement cattle feeding.

In general, forage-based beef production tends to be more ecologically sound and socially responsible than is grain-based cattle feeding. However, forage-finished beef may well be more costly to produce and less acceptable to American consumers than is grain-fed beef. But intensively managed grazing systems offer promise of lower costs and greater production efficiency, resulting in both more pounds of beef per acre and higher quality meat products. Such systems require a much higher level of management and a somewhat higher labor input than do conventional grazing systems. However, the true cost of the human input depends on the nature of competition for management and labor within whole-farm systems. Time demands for managed grazing tend to be more evenly spread over time than do demands of most cropping systems.

Consumer acceptance of grass- and forage-finished beef remains a major challenge. Consumer surveys and test markets have indicated that consumers prefer the appearance, tenderness, and taste of marbled beef produced with grain. Grain-fed beef tends to be higher in saturated fats than is the leaner forage-finished beef, even though attempts to produce and mass-market beef leaner than the USDA Choice grade thus far have met with limited success. Forage-finished beef could be produced without growth hormones and without sub-therapeutic use of antibiotics, which could be positive attributes with health conscious consumers if production and marketing standards were developed to insure such practices. In addition, many processors are currently experimenting with merchandising livestock products through claims that they are produced by environmentally sound and socially responsible means.

Livestock have an important role to play in the development of a sustainable agriculture. Most of the questions of sustainability of livestock production are associated with large-scale, confinement animal feeding operations and most of the opportunities exist for grass- and forage-based livestock operations. Perhaps most important, the challenges of sustainability for grass and forage-based livestock production can be met through more careful and thoughtful management of the animals, grass and forage plants, and the land.

1991

The Tipping Point for Sustainable Farming

14

*F*or more than a decade now, I have been actively involved with the sustainable agriculture *movement.* Yes, I have begun to refer to sustainable agriculture as a movement — an organized effort to promote a particular cause. In the early days, I was optimistic. It seemed that developing a system of farming that was ecologically, socially, and economically sustainable was such a common sense thing to do that everyone would want to become involved with the cause. The USDA had initiated a Low Input Sustainable Agriculture (LISA) program in the late 1980s and had reaffirmed and renamed it as the Sustainable Agriculture Research and Education (SARE) program in the 1990 Farm Bill. Missouri, with its diverse agricultural resource base and its thousands of small farms, seemed to be fertile ground for this new common sense approach to farming. However, my early enthusiasm was soon dampened by the staunch defenders of the industrial approach to farming that had developed in America over the past 50 years.

To corporate agribusiness, a low input agriculture would mean shrinking profits from sales of commercial fertilizers, pesticides, and most of the other off-farm inputs that farmers have become hooked on over the past fifty years. They weren't going to give up those profits without a fight. It wasn't a matter of principle or ethics — it was strictly economics.

To the larger conventional farmers, sustainable agriculture seemed to be more a threat to their ego than to economics. They weren't even willing to consider the possibility that the way they had learned to farm, and had been farming for years, might not be sustainable over the long run. To them, the question of sustainability carried a presumption of guilt. They were the survivors of years of struggle when most of their neighbors had given up or had gone broke. They had been the winners; they didn't want to change the game.

To most small farmers, sustainable agriculture has always made sense. It wasn't all that different from the way most of them had been trying to farm for years. Perhaps there was more emphasis on environmental issues than some might have liked. But most small farmers knew that they had to take care of the soil and water and be good neighbors if they expected their farms to stay productive and profitable over the long run. Sure, many small farmers were no more concerned about their land, their neighbors, or their communities than were the agribusiness corporations. But most small farmers realized that the industrialization of agriculture had stacked the deck against them; they were more than willing to help change the game.

A lot more farms are small than are large. So, one might still have expected strong public support for the sustainable agriculture movement. However, small farmers don't have much influence in the economic or political arenas. The *agricultural establishment* — including USDA, Land Grant Universities, Farm Bureau Federation, and most farm commodity organizations — has effectively suppressed the potential ground swell of grassroots support for the sustainable agriculture movement. The USDA SARE program has more than tripled in size, from its humble $4 million beginning, but remains well below one percent of the total USDA research and education budget. Most Land Grant Universities have at least "token" sustainable agriculture programs, but none have allowed such programs to detract from their primary agenda of promoting agricultural industrialization through biotechnology and other high-tech production systems. Some state departments of agriculture seem to be more supporting of sustainable agriculture programs, perhaps because they feel a need to be more responsive to voters. But most mainstream farm organizations openly promote the "agricultural industry" while giving only token consideration to the impact of the ultimate corporate takeover of agriculture on the future of farmers.

In spite of powerful opposition, the sustainable agriculture movement continues. While progress has been slow and painful within the agricultural establishment, elsewhere there is growing cause for optimism. In the winter of 2001-2002, I had the rare privilege of attending conferences and various other types of gatherings of people interested in sustainable agriculture almost on a weekly basis. I have crisscrossed the U.S. from Montana to North Carolina, from Pennsylvania to California, and from Texas to Michigan. I have met with Canadians in Saskatchewan, Manitoba, Ontario, Nova Scotia, and Prince Edward Island. I am pleased to report that at the grassroots level the sustainable agriculture movement is alive and well.

Several "sustainable agriculture" conferences now draw more than 1,000 people each year — including the Upper Midwest Organic Growers conference. The California Eco-Farming Conference in Monterey in January pre-registered more than 1,200 and probably had closer to 1,500 in attendance. Conferences drawing 400 to 500 people may not be commonplace, but neither are they rare. The Michigan Organic Farming Conference, for example, drew more than 400 people in early March and the Sustainable Hog Production Summit in New Bern, North Carolina in January drew more than 500 people. The numbers of conferences routinely drawing 100–200 people are too many to count. And the numbers of people attending nearly all such conferences keep growing from each year to the next.

Sustainable agriculture has also become a featured theme at far larger gatherings of farmers, such as the Small Farm Today Conference and Trade Show, which drew more than 3,500 people last year. The Sierra Club and other environmental groups have had numerous conferences across the country promoting sustainable agriculture as an ecologically sound alternative to industrial agriculture. And I have participated in a series of conferences organized by Catholic Rural Life groups, Montana's Association of Churches, and the Missouri Center for Rural Ministries, all advocating sustainable agriculture as a moral response to the current economic crisis in rural America.

Sustainable agriculture is no longer a novelty and the people who attend these conferences include few idealists attending out of idle curiosity. Most of the people who attend are farmers. They want to learn more about what they are already doing or are seriously seeking a new and better way to farm. The sustainable agriculture movement also has strength in its diversity. The people are young and old, male and female, well educated and less well educated, well off and less well off financially. They are a cross section of the people of rural America, although not representative of the existing rural or agricultural power structures. These people are building the future of American farming and of rural America, with very little help from their government, their universities, or anyone else. These people deserve a lot more help than they are getting. But, I truly believe they are going to succeed, with or without help from the establishment.

Progress may seem slow, but I have hopes that we are nearing a "tipping point" in the sustainable agriculture movement. In a recent book by the same name, the author, Malcolm Gladwell, uses the analogy of a disease in explaining what happens at a "tipping point." He describes it as the point at which an infection that has been lingering among the general population suddenly explodes into a full-blown epidemic. He suggests that "epidemics of ideas" reach their tipping points when three conditions are present. First, people who are effective in spreading ideas to others have become "infected" with the idea. Second, people learn to express the idea in a way that "sticks in the minds" of lots of other people. And finally, people who are searching for new ideas to replace the old ones create a hospitable environment for change.

I think all of these tipping point conditions are imminent, if not already present, in the sustainable agriculture movement. More and more people of influence are accepting sustainability as a fundamental guiding principle for life's work. People like Bobby Kennedy, Jr. of the Water Keepers Alliance, Prince Charles of Great Britain, and presidential candidate Ralph Nader are but a few examples of people of prominence who are openly supporting the principles and practices of sustainable agriculture.

More people are beginning to understand that sustainability is not about sacrifice, but is about helping people achieve a higher quality of life through a more enlightened concept of self-interest. For example, Paul Hawkins, author of *Ecology of Commerce* and *Natural Capitalism*, recently said that he no longer talks about environmental protection but instead about enhancing our quality of life through attention to community and stewardship. Hopefully, quality of life is a "stickier" way to describe the ultimate purpose of sustainability.

And finally, more and more people are realizing that industrialization is destroying our civil society and natural ecosystems, and corporatization is destroying our democracy and our national sovereignty. We are in the midst of a great societal transition, and it is changing the ways people are thinking about everything. More and more people are realizing that there is something very wrong in America, and they are ready for fundamental change. This great transition of thought creates a hospitable environment for fundamental change.

Perhaps the sustainable agriculture movement is still at the stage of a "low grade infection." But the "disease" is spreading and infecting more people all across rural America. As we join forces with other sustainability movements, we are helping to infect American society as a whole with the desire for change. At some point in the not too distant future, we will reach the "tipping point." The movement will become an "epidemic of change" sweeping like a virus across American society, infecting all whom it touches with a common sense commitment to a sustainable future.

2001

15 | Soil: The Roots of Sustainable Agriculture

*A*ll life is rooted in the soil. All living things, including humans, need food of one kind or another. Life also depends on air and water, but nothing can live with air and water alone. Living things not directly rooted in the soil — things that live in the sea, on rocks, or on trees, for example — still require minerals from the earth. They must have "soil" from somewhere. Living things other than plants get their food from plants or from other living things that feed on plants; and plants feed on the soil. By one means of another, all life is rooted in the soil. The purpose of a sustainable agriculture is to sustain human life, and thus, sustainable farming also must be rooted in the soil.

I am an economist, not a soil scientist. So, when I write about the soil, I try to stick to the things that almost anyone might already know or at least can understand. As I was doing some reading on the subject of soil, I ran across a delightful little book, *The Great World's Farm,* written by English author, Selina Gaye, around the turn of the 20th century. Back then, people didn't know so much about everything, so they could get more of what they knew about a lot of different things into a little book. The book begins by explaining how soil is formed from rock, proceeds through growth and reproduction of plants and animals, and concludes with cycles of life and the balance of nature. The book stresses throughout that all life is rooted in the soil.

Initially, molten lava covered all of the crust of the earth. So, all soil started out as rock. Most plants had to wait until rock was pulverized into small particles before they could feed on the minerals contained in the rock. Chemical reaction with oxygen and carbon dioxide, wearing away by wind and water, expansion and contraction from heating and cooling, and rock slides and glaciers have all played important roles in transforming the earth's crust from rock into soil. However, living things also help create soil for other living things.

Lichens are a unique sort of plant that can grow directly on rock. Their spores settle on rock and begin to grow. They extract their food by secreting acids, which dissolve the minerals contained in the rock. As lichens grow and die, minerals are left in their remains to provide food for other types of plants. Some plants feeding on dead lichens grow roots capable of penetrating crevices in rocks caused by weathering. Growing roots can split and crumble rock further, exposing more surfaces to weathering, and accelerating the process of "soil making."

Specific types of rock contain limited varieties of minerals and will feed limited varieties of plants — even when pulverized into dust. Many plants require more complex combinations of minerals than are available from any single type of rock. So the soils made from various types of rocks had to be mixed before they would support the variety and complexity of plant life that we have come to associate with nature. Sand and dust can be carried from one place to another by wind and water, mixed with sand and dust from other rocks along the way. Glaciers have also been important in mixing soil. Some of the richest soils in the world are fertile bottomlands along flooding streams and rivers, loess hills that were blown and dropped by the wind, and soil deposits left behind by retreating glaciers.

Quoting from *The Great World's Farm,* "No soil is really fertile, whatever the mineral matter composing it, unless it also contains some amount of organic matter — matter derived from organized, living things, whether animal or vegetable. Organic matter alone is not enough to make a fertile soil, but with less than one-half percent of organic matter, no soil can be cultivated to much purpose." After the mixed soil minerals were bound in place by plants, and successions of plants and animals added organic matter and tilth, the mixtures became what we generally refer to as soil.

The first stages of soil formation are distinguished from the latter stages by at least one important characteristic. The initial dissolving, grinding, and mixing required millions of years, whereas, soil binding and adding organic matter can be accomplished in a matter of decades. Thus, the mineral fraction of soil is a *non-renewable* resource — it cannot be recreated or renewed within any realistic future time frame. Whereas, the organic fraction is a renewable or regenerative resource that can be recreated or renewed over decades or at least over a few generations. Misuse can displace, degrade, or destroy the productivity of both fractions of soils within a matter of years. And once the mineral fraction of soil is lost, its productivity is lost forever.

If there are to be productive soils in the future, we must conserve and make wise use of the soils we have today. The soil that washes down our rivers to the sea is no more renewable than are the fossil fuels that we are mining from ancient deposits within the earth. In spite of our best efforts, some quantity of soil will be lost — at least lost to our use. Thus, our only hope for sustaining soil productivity is to conserve as much soil as we can and to build up soil organic matter and enhance the productivity of the soil that remains.

In times not too long past, the connection between soil and human life was clear and ever present. Little more than a century ago, most people were farmers and those who were not lived close enough to a farm to know that the food that gave them life came from the soil. They knew that if the soil was rich, if the rains came and the temperature was hospitable to plants and animals, food would be bountiful, and there would be plenty to eat. They knew that when droughts came, plants dried out then died, the soil was left bare, and there was little to eat. They knew when the floods came, plants were covered with water and died, the soil was left bare, and there was little to eat. They knew very well that their physical well-being, if not their lives, depended on the things that came from the soil.

Today, the connection between soil and life is no less critical but is no longer so direct or so clear. Most urban dwellers have lost all sense of personal connection to the farm or the soil. During most of the past century, many people living in cities either had lived on a farm at one time or knew someone, usually a close relative, who still lived on a farm. Their connection with farming gave them some understanding of their connectedness with the soil. At least they knew that "land" meant something more than just a place to play or space to be filled with some form of development. But these personal connections have been lost with the aging of urbanization. One of the most common laments among farmers today is that "people no longer know where their food comes from." For most, any real understanding of the direct connection between soil and life has been lost. It's sad but true.

Still, all of life depends upon soil. All life requires food and there is simply no other source of food except living things that depend directly or indirectly on the soil. Farmers are the living beings who care for the land, plant the seeds, and nurture the life that springs from the soil. This foundational principle of natural science, of human health, and of social studies should be taught at every level in every school in the world — beginning in kindergarten and continuing through college. The connection between healthy soils and human health and life is as fundamental as our connection with the air we breathe, the water we drink, and the food we eat. It's just less obvious.

Quite possibly, no aspect of education is more critical to the sustainability of human life on earth than is a broad understanding of the critical linkage between the health and life of soil and the health and life of humans. A sustainable agriculture is but the means by which life is brought from the soil and by which the health of the soil is sustained to support future human life. Even the economic and social dimensions of sustainability may be best understood in terms of ecological principles connecting people with the earth in a web of life. Many students may not be particularly interested in farming, but everyone can relate to food and everyone experiences the earth.

Recently, I was asked to participate in a discussion of future directions for soils programs of the University of Missouri. Some of us suggested that future research and education programs should focus on creating a better understanding, among students and the public alike, of the critical linkages among soil health, human health, and societal health. As scientists have focused ever more narrowly within their respective disciplines, we have degraded the natural productivity of our soils, have destroyed the ability of farms to support rural economies, and have diminished the sustainability of human society. If we are to build a sustainable society, scientists of all disciplines eventually must address the full ecological, economic, and social implications of their work. But the science of sustainability must begin with sustaining the life of our soils — where roots of a sustainable agriculture must grow.

2003

Twenty Years of Sustainable Agriculture

16

*T*he 1985 U.S. Farm Bill contained an obscure provision later dubbed as Low Input Sustainable Agriculture or LISA. This marked the official beginning of the "sustainable agriculture movement." Some consider sustainable agriculture to be a continuation of the organic farming movement of the '50s and '60s. Others argue that both organic and sustainable farming are simply branches of a larger movement that includes all farmers who refused to embrace the chemical-farming technologies that emerged from World War II. The term "sustainable agriculture," however, first came to general public awareness with the LISA program.

Sustainable agriculture was born from the merging of three different streams of agricultural concerns. Organic farmers and environmental groups were concerned with the impacts of agricultural chemicals on the natural environment and on human health. Some conventional farmers and agricultural groups were concerned about the impacts of rising input costs and falling commodity prices on the agricultural economy. Small farmers and rural advocacy groups were concerned about the impacts of agricultural industrialization on farm families, rural communities, and society as a whole. These three groups came together to promote the initial LISA legislation, and later, to defend the LISA program against relentless attacks launched by the agricultural establishment.

Agribusiness was not about to support any government program that promoted the use of fewer purchased inputs, and many in the USDA, Land Grant Universities, and mainstream agricultural organizations lacked the courage to oppose the agribusiness community. But the sustainable agriculture coalition held together well enough to save the political identity of the movement. They redefined and renamed LISA to create the Sustainable Agriculture Research and Education program or SARE. Obviously, the SARE program is not synonymous with the sustainable agriculture movement. But, the persistence of the SARE program, in the face of relentless opposition, bears testimony to the movement's continuing strength and durability.

In the early days, a lot of time and effort was spent trying to define sustainable agriculture. The most basic definition to emerge was, "sustainable agriculture: an agriculture that lasts" — an agriculture that can maintain its productivity and value to society, indefinitely. To be sustainable, agriculture must meet the needs of people of the present, while leaving equal or better opportunities for those of the future.

In order to last, a sustainable agriculture must be ecologically sound, economically viable, and socially responsible. If a system of agriculture destroys the productivity of its natural resource base — water, air, or soil — it eventually will lose its ability to produce, and thus, is not sustainable. If a system of agriculture doesn't meet the needs of society as consumers, producers, and citizens, it will not be supported by society, and thus, is not sustainable. And finally, if a system of agriculture fails financially, it is not sustainable, no matter how ecologically sound or socially responsible it might otherwise have been. All three dimensions of sustainability are necessary, and no one is more important than are the others.

Over the years, the dominant themes of the sustainable agriculture movement have evolved, reflecting increasing information and understanding and changing interests of its advocates. In the early days, much of the emphasis in sustainable agriculture research and education was on alternative farming practices, methods, and systems — soil conservation, nutrient management, integrated pest management, reduced energy use, organic farming, low-input farming systems, integrated farming systems, and so on. Later, the emphasis shifted to economics. Questionable attempts were made early on to compare the economics of conventional and sustainable farming systems. Direct marketing and value-added processing continue to be prominent themes in sustainable agriculture research and education programs. The social dimension of sustainability emerged still later through work relating the impacts of alternative farming systems on the sustainability of rural communities. More recently, emphasis has shifted to sustainable community-based food systems.

Sustainable agriculture policy advocates have supported resource conservation and protection programs, such as the Conservation Reserve Program, Environmental Quality Incentive Program, and the new Conservation Security Program. However, the sustainability policy front has become increasingly difficult, as witnessed by difficulties in passing effective government payment limitations and in funding of Value Added Grants, Country of Origin Labeling, Conservation Security Program, and other programs of potential benefit to smaller, family farms.

The LISA program wasn't funded by Congress until 1989, and it took a while after that to get organized. Since the mid-90s, however, the sustainable agriculture movement has shown impressive growth at the grass roots level all across the country. At least five annual "sustainable agriculture" conferences in the U.S. consistently now draw more than 1,200 participants a year — with a couple drawing 2,500 or more. Equally important, the larger conferences are mostly organized by grass-roots organizations, and the vast majority of attendees are farmers. Sustainable agriculture conferences drawing 400–500 have become fairly common and those drawing 100–250 people per year are too numerous to attempt to count. Increasingly, farming conferences are planned in collaboration with citizen and consumer groups, or farmers are included in conferences sponsored by such groups. Attendance continues to grow, and new conferences emerge each year. Many skeptics thought sustainable agriculture would be but a passing fad. After twenty-years, however, this "grass roots" movement is alive and well.

The frontier of the sustainable agriculture movement has now moved beyond the farm gate and into the food system. Sales through farmers' markets, CSAs, and other direct markets continue to grow. But more sustainable farmers are now beginning to access higher-volume markets — including supermarkets and restaurants. Independent food processors, distributors, and retailers are beginning to realize they face the same kinds of challenges from a corporately controlled, global food system as do independent family farmers. They are beginning to understand they must create unique market niches by meeting the unmet needs of a growing number of consumers who are dissatisfied with the industrial food system of today. These independent retailers, independent processors, and family farmers are forming alliances to create a new sustainable food system.

This new food system is emerging to serve a *new food culture*. A growing number of consumers are concerned about food safety, health, and nutrition and are dissatisfied with the taste, or lack of taste, of many industrial food products. They don't trust the industrial food system. Many willingly pay premium prices for wholesome, nutritious food that really tastes good. They are willing to pay more for crops that are grown organically, without exploiting farm workers or degrading the land. They will pay farmers for the added costs of raising animals on pastures, under humane conditions, without chemicals, without hormones or antibiotics. They are concerned about where their food comes from, how it is produced, who benefits, and who pays the costs — including social and environmental costs. They prefer foods grown locally, because local foods can be fresher and more flavorful, but also because it's easier to build trust through face-to-face relationships with local farmers.

The new food culture is rooted in a search for integrity in food and integrity in relationships among eaters, farmers, and the earth. The greatest challenge confronting sustainable agriculture today is to move into more high-volume markets, thus providing good food for more consumers and creating more economic opportunities for farmers, without compromising the social and ecological integrity of the movement.

In the early days, it was easy to become excited about sustainable agriculture as the obvious future of farming in America. To many of us, it was obvious that an industrial agriculture quite simply was not sustainable and thus should be abandoned as quickly as possible. To others, however, genetic engineering promised a new kind of "technological fix" for a chemically dependent agriculture, perpetuating the illusion of potential productivity from further industrial exploitation. Understandably, sustainable agriculture advocates have become discouraged from time-to-time because of aggressive opposition from some, passive lack of support from others, and considerable public apathy. Admittedly, growth in the movement has seemed painfully slow, but most importantly, the movement has continued to grow.

We need to stop and remind ourselves now and then that great social movements sometimes start slowly. The early Christian movement is said to have grown at a rate of only about three percent per year in the early days, increasing the numbers of Christians by about forty percent each decade. After seven years of recruiting, Mohammed had gained only about a hundred Islamic followers. Obviously, slow starts didn't doom either movement to extinction. The industrial revolution took more than a hundred years to progress from Eli Whitney's cotton gin to Henry Ford's assembly line. Sales of organic foods have been growing at twenty-percent per year for more than a decade, but organics still make up less than two percent of total food sales. I am not suggesting that the sustainability movement will have as much impact on the world as Christianity or Islam, but it could be as important as the industrial revolution. The ultimate importance of a social movement simply cannot be judged by its size after a couple of decades.

The sustainable agriculture movement has come a long way in the past twenty years. The banner of sustainable agriculture was once carried by a small band of activists who were concerned about the growing negative consequences of conventional farming for the land, for rural communities, and for the future of family farms. Those early advocates were joined by small groups of thoughtful farmers, a few government bureaucrats, a handful of university professors, and a dozen or so nonprofit organizations to give birth to a new social movement. After twenty years, that movement now seems destined to reshape the American food culture. It's difficult to imagine what progress toward sustainability another twenty years may bring.

2004

17 | Organic Farming & Sustainability – Revisited

*I*s it necessary to farm organically to farm sustainably? I first addressed this question in *Small Farm Today* back in 1993. However, tremendous growth in the popularity of organic foods and changes in organic farming since then have revived the relevance of the question. Several European countries have since made the transition from conventional to organic farming their top priority for agricultural policies. But will a transition to organic farming ensure sustainability? Many organic farmers in the U.S. have decided to forego organic certification, not only because of the cost but also because they don't believe organic certification ensures sustainability. Organic certification obviously has facilitated the industrialization of organic production, and industrial farming systems clearly are not sustainable. Also, many well-known, long-time advocates of sustainable farming have chosen not to farm organically, with or without certification. So is organic farming *necessary* for sustainability?

I didn't have an unqualified answer in 1993, and I don't have one today. The answer still depends on how we define organic and how we define sustainability. The answers are much clearer to me today, even if not unqualified, simply because the definitions are more clear. Sustainability means meeting the needs of the present without compromising the future. In agriculture, sustainable farms must be capable of maintaining their productivity and value to society indefinitely or permanently. Organic means to be organized or structured as a living, biological organism. In agriculture, organic farms must be managed as living systems, capable of self-renewal, regeneration, and permanence. Thus, *permanence* is the critical link between organics and sustainability.

The confusion regarding sustainability of organic farming stems from confusion regarding the meaning for organic farming. If organic farming simply means farming without synthetic chemicals, then organic systems are not necessarily sustainable. This is readily attested to by the past fall of great civilizations due to unsustainable farming practices in times long before agrichemicals. If organic farming means farming according to some formula or rigid set of rules and regulations, then organic does not ensure sustainability, any more so than rigid sets of rules and regulations ensure the health and well-being of plants, animals, children, societies, or any other living organism or organization. If farming organically means farming for permanence, then and only then, farming organically ensures sustainability.

The link between organic farming and permanence is deeply rooted in the history of the organic farming movement. In a landmark series of lectures in 1924, Rudolph Steiner, the father of biodynamic farming, wrote, "A farm is healthy only as much as it becomes an organism in itself — an individualized, diverse ecosystem guided by the farmer, standing in living interaction with the larger ecological, social, economic, and spiritual realities of which it is part." To Steiner, the word *organic* described the farm as a living system, as an organism. He also considered the relationships among the farm, farmer, food, and eater to be *divinely* determined. He was concerned that food grown on the increasingly impoverished soil of conventional farms could not sustain either physical health or spiritual health.

Early advocates of organic farming believed that human health was directly connected to the health of the soil. A noted University of Missouri soil scientist, William Albrecht, wrote in 1952, "Human nutrition as a struggle for complete proteins goes back . . . to fertile soils alone, on which plants can create proteins in all completeness." Organic pioneer and publisher of *Organic Farming* magazine, J.I. Rodale, wrote, "The *organiculturist* farmer must realize that in him is placed a sacred trust, the task of producing food that will impart health to the people who consume it. As a patriotic duty, he assumes an obligation to preserve the fertility of the soil, a precious heritage that he must pass on, undefiled and even enriched, to subsequent generations."

Sir Albert Howard, another organic pioneer, also emphasized intergenerational responsibility as the core principle of organic agriculture. Howard began his book, *An Agricultural Testament*, with the assertion,

"The maintenance of the fertility of the soil is the first condition of any permanent system of agriculture." In his opening chapter, he contrasted the permanent agriculture of the Orient with the agricultural decline that led to the fall of Rome. He wrote, "The peasants of China, who pay great attention to the return of all wastes to the land, come nearest to the ideal set by Nature. They have maintained a large population on the land without any falling off in fertility. The agriculture of ancient Rome failed because it was unable to maintain the soil in a fertile condition." Historian, G.T. Wrench, wrote of the fall of Rome, "Money, profit, the accumulation of capital and luxury, became the objects of landowning and not the great virtues of the soil and the farmers of few acres." Howard concluded, "The farmers of the West are repeating the mistakes made by Imperial Rome."

Thus, the historic purpose of organic farming was *permanence* — to ensure the sustainability of agriculture, and through agriculture, the sustainability of human society. Only living organisms, including living organizations, have the capacity for self-renewal and regeneration, and thus, the capacity for permanence. Non-living systems inevitably tend toward entropy, "the ultimate state reached in degradation of matter and energy; a state of inert uniformity of component elements; absence of form, pattern, hierarchy, or differentiation." Living systems are capable of permanence because they are capable of capturing and storing solar energy to offset this inevitable degradation of matter and energy. Non-living systems lack this capacity. Thus, permanence is inherently dependent on healthy, living, organic systems of production, which are capable of restoring the nutritional energy inevitably lost in the natural tendency toward entropy. Only living, organic systems are capable of permanence.

Back to the initial questions, a transition to organic farming will not necessarily ensure sustainability unless the organic farms are capable of permanence. Organic standards will not ensure sustainability because permanence, being reliant on living systems, cannot be ensured through adherence to a rigid set of rules and regulations. Organic farming is *sufficient* to ensure sustainability, but only if organic is defined to mean *permanent*. And finally, organic farming is also *necessary* to ensure sustainability, but again, the definition of organic is critical in drawing this final conclusion.

If organic defines a particular way of thinking — specifically, nurturing the farm as a living organism or system rather than managing it as machine or factory — then organic is *necessary* for sustainability. Mechanisms are incapable of self-renewal and regeneration and thus are inherently unsustainable; they inevitably tend toward entropy. If on the other hand, organic farming rigidly prohibits the use of specific farming practices and chemical inputs, then the answer is not quite so clear.

Our bodies are the living organisms that we know best. Apparently, most of us do not believe the health, productivity, and regenerative capacity of our bodies require, or are even best served, by the rigid prohibition of synthetic chemicals or "unnatural" medical procedures. When we have a health problem that can be "fixed" by modern medicine, we are unwilling to suffer or die just because the "fix" is not organic or natural. But neither do we believe that chemical dependency or artificial life support are capable of fulfilling our long-term physical or mental needs. Many of us would rather suffer occasional physical illness, mental depression, or even death than to live *artificially*. In addition, unhealthy "fixes" are not limited to inorganic or artificial means, as attested to by addictions to tobacco and alcohol or the relentless pursuits of sensual pleasures.

Many of us believe that both individual and societal well-being are best served by natural, organic means — through proper diet, exercise, intellectual stimulation, and positive personal and spiritual relationships. But when we are unable to maintain our health by natural means, we are not opposed to utilizing "unnatural" means of restoring our bodies or minds to health. Even in situations that are not life threatening, many of us are not opposed to the occasional use of "unnatural" means of easing discomfort — such aspirins and antacids. We believe that "unnatural" means can be used to improve long run human health and well-being, as long as they don't become substitutes for healthy diets and lifestyles.

These same principles would seem relevant to healthy, organic farming systems. Perhaps organic consumers insist on total abstinence from agrichemicals and specific production practices because they don't believe organic farmers can be trusted to use such things without becoming dependent on them. Many people also abstain from tobacco, alcohol, and even coffee for the same reason; they fear becoming dependent. Perhaps they are right. However, the problem is a lack of trust or confidence, not a matter of total abstinence being necessary to preserve health.

So I will leave the question of *necessity* versus *sufficiency* unanswered, at least for now. The answer seems to depend on whether chemical use inevitably leads to abuse and dependency. I believe the answer to that question depends entirely on the individual. If you are committed to sustainability and believe that use of synthetic chemicals or other conventional farming practices inevitably leads to abuse and dependency, then insist on *abstinence,* but also insist on *permanence.* If you believe agrichemicals and other "unnatural" remedies to farming problems can be used responsibly, then insist on *integrity,* but also insist on *permanence.* I personally believe restoring integrity to food and farming systems is more important that defining and enforcing prohibitions and restrictions. Regardless of which approach you prefer, permanence is both necessary and sufficient for sustainability.

2005

MANAGEMENT

18 A Chance for Small Farmers to Get a Bigger Piece of the Pie

*B*y one means or another, farming systems that are capable of sustaining society over the long run must be capable of sustaining individual farmers in the short run. Much of the economic emphasis of sustainable agriculture has been on reducing farmers' costs of purchased inputs. However, greater market value may be even more important than lower costs in making ecologically sound systems of farming both economically viable and socially supportive.

Conventional farmers, for the most part, have limited their activities to production and marketing of raw agricultural commodities such as corn, soybeans, hogs, and cattle. Over time, many farmers have expanded their operations horizontally, producing more on larger farms as profit margins per unit or production are squeezed by increasing competition. On the other hand, an increasing number of non-conventional farmers are finding ways to expand vertically, by producing their own inputs and marketing as well as processing and distributing their own products, rather than increasing the size of their farming operations. By expanding vertically, they widen their operation margins by moving the point of first sale upward toward the ultimate consumer through activities that add value, and moving direct costs downward through activities that reduce purchased inputs. The number of farmers able to compete in large-scale production of raw agricultural commodities will continue to decline in the foreseeable future. The economic future for most farmers, then, will depend on their ability to expand vertically rather than horizontally.

The primary public mandate for U.S. agriculture throughout the twentieth century was to support industrial development of the U.S. economy. Industrialization required "manpower" to run the factories and discretionary consumer income to buy the things that factories produce. At the beginning of the twentieth century, a large proportion of the U.S. work force was engaged in farming and a large proportion of consumers' incomes was spent on food and fiber. Agriculture had to be made more efficient to reduce agriculture's claim on consumers' incomes and to free farmers and their families to work in the factories and offices of an industrial economy.

Government programs for agriculture were focused on increased agricultural productivity. Commodity programs created a stable market environment which encouraged specialization and investment in specialized facilities and equipment. Research and education were funded to develop new technologies that would substitute mechanization and commercial inputs for farm labor and management. Profits motivated farmers to adopt these new technologies. However, profits accrued only to the early adopters. Production increasing technologies reduced farmers' costs, leaving a profit gap between production costs and prices. But as more farmers adopted a given technology, production increased and prices fell, first squeezing and then eliminating the previous margins of profit. The incentive for later adopters was survival rather than profitability, and those who adopted too late didn't survive. This is the process by which farmers were "freed" from farming, so they could pursue other occupations.

As each new round of profits per bushel or per hundredweight became smaller, farmers had to increase production more and do it more quickly just to maintain their levels of total profit or net income. All but a few farmers now find themselves "running faster and faster just to stay in the same place." Farmers are forced to buy out their faltering neighbors' farms just to stay in business themselves. As the gap between increasing input costs and falling prices narrows, this vicious cycle becomes even more vicious. Margins between input costs and commodity prices have been squeezed to the point where there is now very little left to be squeezed out.

Agriculture has fulfilled its public mandate for the twentieth century. Workers have been provided for factories and offices. Expenditures on food have dropped. A century ago, the 1890 U.S. Census indicated that more than approximately 22 million people (40 percent of the population) lived on farms. A hundred years later, only 4.6 million people (less than 2 percent of total U.S. population) live on farms. In addition, families living on farms today earn more than 90 percent of their family income from non-farm sources. Food production probably claimed close to 50 percent of the nation's resources in 1890 with resources used in transportation and marketing added to those in farm production.

A hundred years later, food costs amounted to less than 12 percent of average consumers' incomes. Farmers received only about 20 cents of each dollar spent for food. The rest, 80 cents, went to marketing firms. In addition, farmers got to keep only about half of what they receive, or 10 cents of each dollar that consumers spend on food while the other 10 cents paid for purchased inputs including rent, hired labor, and interest on borrowed money. The farmer's share of total consumer expenditures, including food and all other items, was less than 1.5 percent.

Society now appears to be giving agriculture a new, much broader mandate for the future. The new mandate is to develop a food and fiber system which will continue to be productive but will also be ecologically sound, economically viable, socially supportive and, thus, sustainable. Consumers don't want their food costs to climb back to percentage levels of a few decades ago, but society as a whole has very little left to be gained from further increases in the productivity of agriculture. If the efficiency of farm-based production activities were increased by an additional 50 percent, total costs of food production would drop by only five percent. Agriculture's claim to total consumer expenditures would drop by less than one percent. Rising environmental and social costs of further agricultural industrialization must now be weighted against potential efficiency gains much smaller than those of the past.

The new social mandate for U.S. agriculture represents new challenges for farmers. But with the challenge comes new opportunities. Farmers, like consumers, have relatively little to gain from further increases in productivity. The odds of squeezing profits out of the 90 percent of food costs currently accounted for by input and marketing costs seem much better than the odds of squeezing still more profits out of the ten percent that currently goes to farmers. The new challenge to farmers is to widen, rather than narrow, the gap between the cost of purchased inputs and the value of their products.

The most immediate means of increasing farmers' share of the agricultural pie is to manage farm inputs more effectively using existing technologies within conventional farming systems. Application rates, timing, and placement of fertilizer are some of the most obvious areas for potential improvement. For example, nitrogen applied in the right amount at the right time, and at the right place, is more likely to be used by the plant and less likely to contaminate groundwater or streams. Wasted nitrogen contributes to costs but not to yields, reducing the net economic returns of crop production. Thus, more efficient nitrogen application through soil testing, tissue testing, banding, and split applications could increase the ecologic and economic sustainability of crop production systems. Similar possibilities exist for the use of insecticides, herbicides, and other pesticides, even in specialized farming operations. Pesticides applied at the right time and right place may control pests more effectively at lower rates of application. More effective pest control at lower levels of use reduces environmental risk and increases economic sustainability.

Resource conservation may also be achieved through more efficient resource management. For example, efficient irrigation scheduling may reduce crop stress while cutting the use of water and energy. Greater predictability of growth may allow efficient use of fertilizer and other inputs as well. Reduced tillage can reduce soil loss and cut energy inputs without sacrificing profitability in many situations.

Cost savings from input management can be achieved without changing the fundamental nature of farming systems. However, the greatest promise for sustainable profitability seems to lie with the development of more efficient diversified systems of farming. Diversified systems are generally conceded to be more ecologically sound than specialized systems because they rely less on the inputs associated with environmental risks. However, diversified farming has been abandoned by many farmers in the past in favor of greater specialization, in their pursuit of greater economic efficiency.

Gains from specialization are undeniable but are not the only route to greater economic efficiency. Farming systems can also be made more efficient through integration of diversity. The productivity of a well-integrated farming system can be greater than the sum of the products of the individual farming components. This phenomenon is called synergism. Specialized farming systems sacrifice the potential gains from synergistic interaction among the various components that are possible with more diversified farming systems.

An obvious example of synergism is the interaction between livestock and crop rotations that include high quality legume forage crops. Livestock add value to the forage and recycle nutrients back to the soil in the form of manure. Legumes add nitrogen to the soil, break row crop pest cycles, and provide feed for the livestock. Livestock without high quality legume pastures may not be profitable. Legumes in rotations without livestock may not be profitable. However, integrated livestock and legume rotation systems may add profitability to the total farming operation. This is but one example of the potential synergistic gains from integrated farming systems.

Financial risks are another important, but often overlooked, consideration in diversification. Risks may be far greater in a specialized farming operation than in a diversified farming system with the same basic level of uncertainty in each system component. The economic ups and downs of individual enterprises within a whole farm system may tend to be offsetting. Profits from one enterprise may offset losses from another. However, in specialized systems of farming it is either "feast or famine," depending on the economics of the dominant farm enterprise in a given year.

Synergistic farming systems are made up of system components which complement, coordinate, correlate, conserve, and contribute. Such components complement by completing nutrient and water cycles to increase efficiency and reduce wastes. Such systems use land and labor more efficiently by coordinating farming activities to keep all resources fully employed without overextending any. Low or negative correlations among farm system components ensure offsetting production and price risks, enhancing stability and reducing financial risks. In addition, diversified, synergistic systems conserve their resource base by combining components which contribute to achievement of the multiple ecologic and economic objectives of sustainability rather than exploitation of resources for unsustainable short-run profits. Farmers can enhance their profit potential through better management of farm inputs and resources.

However, even greater potential for improving farming profits lies in integrating upward, into the marketing system. Agricultural marketing includes all the various activities involved in the transformation of raw farm commodities into finished food and fiber products. The most obvious aspect of this transformation is a change in physical appearance or form. Form-changing activities for agricultural commodities range from washing and grading apples to processing wheat into Wheaties. Another important marketing function is transportation. Agricultural commodities must somehow get from the farms where they are grown to the homes where they are consumed, in some cases moving across a country or halfway around the world. Time is another important aspect of marketing. Many agricultural commodities must be harvested at a specific time, but can be stored for later use and in some cases be consumed year-round.

Finally, in a specialized economy, most consumers are not producers. Marketing involves the transfer of ownership or possession from those who produce, ultimately, to those who consume.

Market transformations (changes in form, place, time, and ownership) affect the value of commodities as they move through the marketing system. Each of these functions also has an associated cost. Profits result whenever the value added by marketing functions such as processing, transportation, storage, or brokerage, is greater than the cost of performing those functions. These basic principles of marketing may seem simplistic; however, they are the fundamental concepts upon which profitable vertical expansion of farming operations must be built.

Marketing, to most farmers, means commodity marketing. They produce commodities such as corn, wheat, hogs, or cattle. One farmer's No. 2 grade yellow corn is pretty much like any other farmer's No. 2 yellow corn. One cattle feeder's 1100 lb. choice steers are a lot like steers of a similar weight and grade from any other feedlot. Thus, the commodities one farmer has to offer for sale are freely interchangeable with commodities offered for sale by many other farmers, oftentimes including farmers on another continent. Commodity markets tend to be highly competitive because there are many buyers and sellers of the same basic commodity. Price differences among different market locations rarely exceed transportation costs and price increases after harvest tend to just about equal storage costs. Farmers' opportunities to increase profits through commodity marketing are very limited.

Product marketing is different from commodity marketing. Commodities are alike, but products are different. In marketing jargon, products are commodities that have been differentiated to give them distinct quality characteristics and thus distinct market values. These differences may be tangible in nature (as in nutrient values of foods) or intangible (as in consumer acceptance created by brand advertising). Differentiation creates a more or less unique market niche for a product, taking it out of direct competition of other products. The greater the differentiation, the greater will be the potential for profits. Products that have a few good substitutes may command a substantial price premium over less acceptable alternatives. However, consumers will not pay much more for a product that has good substitutes. Products may be differentiated with respect to anything that affects value including form, time, place, and possession.

Many of the farmers who exemplify sustainable agriculture today produce and market products rather than commodities. Many of those farmers sell at least a portion of their products directly to consumers as certified organic produce or as products produced without chemical pesticides. Many others make smaller, diversified farming operations economically viable by performing processing, transporting, storing, or merchandizing activities in addition to production. Still others have found profitable niche markets for commodities that can be produced without significant environmental risks. Many non-conventional alternative farmers sustain their operations by practicing the principles of good marketing.

Examples of successful small farmers are not difficult to find in any part of the United States. Ron Macher of the *Small Farm Today* magazine refers to the new breed of successful small farmers as "agripreneurs." He characterizes these new farmers as risk takers who are not afraid to try new things or to try old things in new ways. They are always searching for solutions and are willing to learn from others. They are marketers, not just growers. They make commitments to deliver on schedule and put the needs of their customers ahead of their own convenience. They have learned how to set prices for the things they produce rather than accept whatever the market offers.

Macher has observed that agripreneurs often are people who want a better life for their children — a place where the children can develop a work ethic and a set of values and an opportunity for the family to work and play together. They do not consider hard work to be a degrading way of life. He also outlines some basic principles of agripreneurship. First, there are no outside experts who have all the answers or new technologies that can make farms profitable. Profitability is the responsibility of the agripreneurs. *Gross* income may determine the size of the business, but *net* income determines the size of its profits. A little business with wide profit margins can make just as much money as a big business with narrow profit margins. And there is a lot less risk of total failure when the margins are wide. Total production may be determined by "how much" land is used, but productivity is determined by "how well" land is used. In the long run, the land will sustain society only if farmers are able to sustain the productivity of the land. And society must be sustainable if farmers are to be able to sustain the land.

Successful family farms of the future may be quite different from family farms of the past. The major distinctions between the two will be in their ways of thinking. Farmers with a conventional mind-set will continue to produce basic commodities for many years to come. However, the most successful new farmers of the twenty-first century may be the agripreneurs. Perhaps the most common piece of advice given to those who would be agripreneurs is, "Don't think like a conventional farmer." Agripreneurs think in terms of producing value rather than growing crops or livestock.

Agripreneurship, like sustainable agriculture, is part of the new paradigm for agriculture. New paradigms require a lot of rethinking and sometimes a whole new beginning. But farmers who succeed in getting a larger piece of the agricultural pie of the future may be those who expand vertically rather than horizontally, by becoming agripreneurs.

1994

19 | Making a Living on a Small Farm

*I*n times past, forty acres, a mule, and a lot of hard work were all that it took to make a living on a farm. But those times are gone. A family could live well on a lot less money in those times, but hard work also was worth a lot more back then — regardless of whether it was done by a mule or by a man. The conventional wisdom was that anyone who was willing to work hard enough could make it on the farm. During the financial crisis of the 1980s, many farmers virtually "worked themselves to death" trying to save their farm. If they could just work hard enough, they could make it. But they couldn't — they went broke.

Work simply isn't worth as much as it once was, at least not on the farm. Tractors took the place of horses and mules. Other machinery and equipment took most of the work out of most jobs around the farm. Physical labor isn't worth any more than the cost of using a machine to do the same job, maybe even less, because machines are less bothersome to fix or replace and far easier to manage than are humans.

Mechanization made farming easier. Farmers became machine operators rather than laborers. But a mechanized farmer could farm a lot more land or raise a lot more livestock than could a farmer doing everything by hand. And farmers still had to work full-time if they expected to make a full-time living by farming. So a full-time mechanized farmer had to have a lot more land and a lot more capital tied up in machinery and equipment, just to make a living. With mechanization, many farms became larger, and it became more difficult to make a living on a small farm.

Agricultural chemicals also made farming easier, taking some additional labor out of farming, but mostly, making a farm far easier to manage. A farmer didn't need to know nearly as much about maintaining the natural fertility of the soil; they could take a soil test and apply the right fertilizers. They could specialize in crops or livestock; they didn't need manure to go back onto the fields to maintain fertility. Farmers didn't need to know how to till the fields to control weeds; they could spray with herbicides. They didn't need to understand how to use crop rotations to control weeds, insects, and other pests; they could use commercial pesticides. Livestock farmers didn't need to know how to keep their animals healthy and growing; they had antibiotics and hormones to fill in the gaps in their knowledge. Farmers now could farm by a recipe or formula. As farms became easier to manage, each farmer was able to farm more land or raise more livestock. However, a farmer still had to work full-time to earn a full-time living. So with increasing use of agricultural chemicals, farms grew still larger, and it became still more difficult to make a living on a small farm.

In economic terms, there are only four basic factors of production, or four basic ingredients in any production process — land, labor, capital, and management. Over time, machines, agri-chemicals, and other technologies have resulted in substitution of capital and land for labor and management. Consequently, a typical full-time farm today requires far more land and capital than fifty years ago. It takes far more money to buy and operate a farm today because of high land and equipment costs and expenses for fertilizers, pesticides, and other commercial inputs. But on a typical farm today, labor and management are far less important than fifty years ago. If a farmer has enough land and enough money to buy the latest equipment and technology, they don't have to work much or even think much, except about how to manage their money.

In economic terms, each of the four factors of production earns something in return for its contribution. Land earns rent, labor earns wages, capital earns interest, and management earns a salary. Profit or loss is the reward or penalty for taking the risk associated with investing land, labor, capital, and management in an enterprise without knowing whether the net results will be positive or negative. Profit is the reward for taking the risk of farming rather than renting the land, putting the money in an insured certificate of deposit, and working for someone else. In general, each factor earns a return in relation to its contribution to the production process.

As the nature of farming has changed, the returns to land and capital have grown, and the returns to labor and management have declined. It isn't necessary to quote statistics; it's just plain common sense. Returns to labor and management are returns to the farmer — to the human investment in a farming operation. The land and capital can be owned by anyone — increasingly by someone other than the farmer. Actual farming is about working and thinking — labor and management. And in general, the return to *farming* can be no more than proportional to the working and thinking done by the farmer. If there isn't much working and thinking going into producing a crop or a batch of livestock, there isn't going to be much in it for the farmer; and it will be tough to make a living without a lot more land and capital. Farmers who don't do much working or thinking simply can't expect to make a living on a small farm.

The ultimate *low-return agriculture* is contract production. Farmers are being told that the only way they can remain competitive in agriculture is by signing a comprehensive production contract with one of the giant agribusiness corporations. But farmers need to stop and think, "Who can logically expect to benefit from contract production?" Under most contracts, the corporation arranges for capital — mostly loans to be repaid by the grower. The corporation provides all of the technology — genetics, equipment, feed, health care, and so on. And the corporation provides virtually all of the management; the growers mainly do what they are told to do. The grower provides the labor, but the highly mechanized operations require little labor. Contract livestock or poultry operations require little land, although the grower is expected to find some place to dispose of manure. In summary, the grower provides a small amount of equity capital, a small amount of land, and some low-skilled labor. The corporation provides everything else. The grower gets a fixed amount per animal produced, regardless of costs or price, so the contractor even takes most of the risk. So who is going to benefit from a corporate contract operation? Certainly not the grower; the grower doesn't do anything that would justify making a living in such an operation.

So what does all this say about making a living on a small farm? It says small farmers have to put a lot more of themselves into their operations — a lot more management and labor — than do most farmers today. It says that a farmer can't expect to make a decent living if someone else makes all of the important decisions, and they only contribute some low-skilled labor. It says that farmers must rely on management and labor far more and rely on land and capital far less if they expect to make a living on a small farm. It says that the way to turn a small farm into a full-time farming operation is to find ways to substitute management and labor for land and capital.

There is a limit to how hard anyone can work, or more important, would want to work on a farm. Working harder is still not the secret to making a living on a small farm, even though most of us would be better off if we did a bit more physical labor and a bit less sitting. However, *thinking* is potentially far more productive and is far less limiting than is working. So the key to making a living on a small farm is *more-intensive* management mixed with an appropriate amount of *skilled* labor. A small farmer has less land and capital so they have to do more thinking and decision making per acre or dollar invested, and they have to be willing to work when working is the logical thing to do. They have to put more of themselves into it if they expect to get more for themselves out of it. The successful farmer of the future might quite accurately be labeled a *thinking worker* or a *working thinker*. The key is to do both together, simultaneously, in harmony.

It takes more thinking to work with nature to reduce costs of inputs and increase profits while taking care of the land — more *eyes per acre* as Wes Jackson says. It takes more thinking to find and keep customers who want, and are willing to pay for, the things a small farmer can produce in harmony with nature — *relationship marketing* as Joel Salatin calls it. It takes more thinking to fit your unique talents and skills as a farmer to the needs of your land, to your particular customers and your community — *linking people, purpose, and place*. Literally thousands of these thinking workers are on small farms today all across the land, putting more of themselves into their operations and getting more for themselves in return. Each is doing something different, but one-by-one, they are finding ways to make a good living on a small farm.

2000

20 Sustainable Farm Management

A farm is an organization — a purposeful arrangement of diverse elements into a coherent whole. A farm is an arrangement of land, plants, animals, buildings, equipment, and people, designed to meet specific human needs. Any organization, including a farm, is defined as much by the arrangement of its different elements or components as by the components that comprise the whole. Farm management is thus the science and art of arranging the various components of a farm so it may better fulfill its purpose.

The sustainability of any organization ultimately depends on its regenerative capacity. Only living organisms are capable of regeneration. A sustainable farm must be managed as a living organization. In living organisms, components or parts are inseparable aspects of the whole. Sustainable farming requires a holistic approach to farm management — an approach that manages the farm as a whole rather than as a collection of separable components or parts. The holistic farm manager looks for opportunities to rearrange diverse farm enterprises, methods, and practices across space, over time, and among individuals, to improve the effectiveness with which the various components work together to fulfill the purpose of the farm.

Holistic management might seem a bit challenging at first. Once understood, however, it's mostly common sense. The book, *Holistic Management,* by Alan Savory and Jody Butterfield, provides an excellent framework for managing holistically for those who need a well-defined structure and detailed approach to decision making. However, the basic principles and strategies of holistic management are quite straightforward.

The holistic farm manager must first have a thorough understanding of the purpose of the farm organization and the principles by which it must operate. The importance of purpose and principles in holistic management cannot be overemphasized. In very basic terms, the holistic purpose of a farm must be defined in terms of the quality of life the farm is to provide — economically, socially, and ecologically. The principles of holistic management are the principles by which the various components of a sustainable farm must function. The principles must include the fundamental laws of nature, including human nature, which cannot be violated without threatening the sustainability of the farm. The principles of sustainability are rooted in basic physics, biology, and psychology, but are mostly common sense.

Next, the holistic farm manager must have a firm grasp of the farm organization as a whole, meaning, how the various farm enterprises, methods, and practices fit together. He or she must understand not only the function of each component, but also how the various functional components work together in fulfilling the purpose of the farm organization. The essence of a sustainable farm is far more than the simple sum of its parts.

With an understanding of purpose, principles, and the organizational whole, decisions can be made incrementally to improve overall organizational performance. This approach to management, called partial budgeting in economics, can be used to improve the expected performance of a farm during the initial planning process, as well as for operational decisions of an ongoing farming operation. All that is required is an existing situation to serve as a point of departure.

Change invariably is motivated by a desire either to deal with a perceived problem or to realize a potential opportunity. Perceived problems and opportunities in sustainable organizations may be economic, ecological, or social in nature. Anything that might allow the organization to fulfill its purpose more effectively represents a logical opportunity for change. Partial budgeting allows the manager to evaluate the impacts of potential change on the organization as a whole, without reexamining all aspects of the whole organization. Typically, partial budgeting has been used to evaluate economic impacts, but the process is equally well suited to evaluate social and ecological impacts.

In partial budgeting, the manager asks a series of questions, the answers to which, taken together, indicate the advisability of the proposed change. Beginning with economics, what will be the potential "direct, economic benefit" of the change? For example, if a new crop is added to a crop rotation, what will be the expected increase in farm revenues? Next, what will be the "direct, economic costs" of the change, or what are the expected dollar and cent costs of production? To this point, the process is a single enterprise budgeting problem — what are the expected costs and returns of a new enterprise?

Next, however, the farm manager must consider the potential indirect economic benefits and costs — the positive and negative impacts of an enterprise on the rest of the farm organization. "Indirect economic benefits" reflect increases in net returns associated with *other enterprises* resulting from the proposed change. Perhaps a new animal enterprise will produce a by-product, such as manure that can be used as an input for another farm enterprise, thus decreasing its production costs. Or maybe a new vegetable crop will add variety to a market garden farm, adding value to its entire line of produce for sale. Regardless, the potential contributions of new enterprises to other components of the organization are an important aspect of holistic management.

New enterprises may also result in "indirect economic costs." Obviously, new economic enterprises may compete for resources — land, time, money — currently committed to other enterprises, and thus may reduce the efficiency and profitability of those enterprises. Regardless of the source, potential negative economic impacts of new enterprises on other components of the organization can be a deciding factor in the decision making process.

Finally, "direct economic costs" are subtracted from "direct economic benefits," and the "indirect economic costs" are subtracted from "indirect economic benefits," and the two resulting net values are added together. If the sum of "direct" and "indirect" net economic benefits is positive, the new enterprise would be expected to increase the economic performance of the organization as a whole. If the sum of the two is negative, the expected economic impact of the change on the organization as a whole would be negative.

In holistic management, the motive for changes may be ecological or social as well as economic. Even those changes motivated by economic problems or opportunities may have significant ecological or social implications for the organization. So, regardless of the primary motivation, the partial budgeting process must include ecological and social considerations. The conceptual process is the same for estimating economic impacts; the ecological and social impacts are just more difficult to quantify. Also, in the case of ecological and social benefits and costs, the distinction between "direct" and "indirect" costs and benefits also seems less clear. Regardless of the process, the holistic manager must make an assessment of the "net social benefits" and "net ecological benefits," to be balanced with the "net economic benefit."

The holistic manager must ask of any proposed change, what will be the "social benefits"? How will this change improve relationships among people — among people on the farm and between those on the farm and others? How will it help build trust and interdependence? How will these improved relationships help the organization fulfill its social purpose — enhance social quality of life — both now and in the future?

Next, what are the "social costs"? How will this change detract from the quality of relationships and quality of life? How much time will it take away from time now spent with family, friends, or community? How does it threaten trust and interdependence? The "social costs" must be balanced against the "social benefits" to derive some assessment of the "net social benefits" — which may be either positive or negative.

The holistic manager must ask of any proposed change, what will be the "ecological benefits"? How will this change improve the ecological integrity of the organization, for the benefit of those on the farm and for others, both now and in the future? How will this change contribute to the ethical and moral integrity of the organization? How does it help to conserve and regenerate the resources of the land? How will it help the farm fulfill its ecological purpose — including the ethical quality of life — both now and in the future?

Next, what are the anticipated "ecological costs"? How does this change threaten the natural environment or degrade the natural resource base? In what ways does it raise ethical and moral questions about the organization? How might this diminish the quality of life of people within and outside the organization? How might this change detract from the ecological purpose of the organization — both now and in the future? The "ecological costs" are then balanced against the "ecological benefits" to derive an assessment of the "new ecological benefits" — which again may be either positive or negative.

In holistic management, the final step in the partial budgeting process is to consider the balance among "net economic benefits, net social benefits, and net ecological benefits." Unfortunately, there is no *objective* means of calculating a single expected "net total benefit." For this, the holistic decision maker will simply have to use his or her common sense. However, with an understanding of the organizational whole, of its fundamental purpose and the principles by which it must operate, and with a thoughtfully derived set of economic, ecological, and social net benefits, common sense decisions should be made easier.

Of course, a change in any part of a whole may result in changes to the whole that cannot be easily anticipated in advance. So the results of each decision should be monitored for unanticipated consequences — particularly for unanticipated negative consequences. Savory, refers to this as "assuming that you are wrong" until proven right. Regardless, the sustainable farm manager must constantly monitor the performance of the farming operation in relation to its purpose and principles, be quick to admit mistakes, and slow to conclude success. Managing for sustainability, like life, is a continuing process of learning.

2003

21 | Many Farms Are Too Big to Survive

Get big or get out" is a refrain with which American farmers are all too familiar. Small farms are seen as being too small to survive, and thus, unworthy of serious consideration. For example, government programs, including publicly funded research and education, tend to focus on large, commercial agricultural operations as the future of American agriculture. In fact, the opposite is true. Most large, commercial farms today are too big to survive. Small farms are the future of farming in America.

Although the large commercial farming operations may appear to be productive and profitable, they are simply too large to be sustainable over time. Sustainable farming operations must be ecologically sound and socially responsible if they are to be economically viable, and thus, sustainable. As a farm expands beyond the natural productivity capacity of its ecological and social niche, it must turn to extraction and exploitation as a means of maintaining its output. Production based on extraction and exploitation quite simply is not sustainable. Many large, commercial farms today have expanded beyond their naturally healthy size. Their ecological, social, and economic health is declining each year. They are dying a slow and destructive death.

Their short run profitability is achieved by exploiting and degrading the natural resource base upon which their productivity ultimately depends. On many of these farms, for example, soil is eroding at rates far in excess of its natural regenerative ability, and agricultural chemicals are polluting groundwater and streams and destroying the biological life of the soil. Many large agricultural operations generate short run profits by exploiting and degrading the quality of life of the people who farm, the people of the surrounding rural communities, and people of society in general. In addition, the occupation of farming is being de-skilled through corporate contractual arrangements, which reduce the function of farming to that of low-skilled, low-paid labor. Consequently, the productivity and profitability of many large, commercial farming operations are not sustainable over time, no matter how promising they may seem today.

Why do farmers choose to operate in ways that ultimately destroy the economic viability of their farms? The answer is because they have lost sight of the fact that a farm is a living thing. In the minds of many farmers today, farms are simply factories without roofs, and fields and feedlots are nothing more than biological assembly lines. Agriculture is just another industry, and a successful farm must be run like any other business. There is no natural limit to the size of industrial business organizations — the bigger they are, the more successful they are considered to be. Thus, farmers who have this industrial mindset see no natural limit to the size of their farming operations — the bigger the farm, the more successful the farmer.

Giantism — meaning fewer, larger businesses — is a classic symptom of industrialization. Industrialization — with its specialization, standardization, and consolidation of control — recognizes no natural limits to size. As production becomes increasingly specialized, each specialized element is standardized, routinized, and mechanized, allowing ever-larger operations to be consolidated under the control of a single decision maker. The continuing consolidation of giant corporations today, many of which are already multinational in scope, provides clear evidence of the lack of natural limits to size for industrial business organizations. In agriculture, thousands of production units are now controlled by a few giant business organizations, providing equally clear evidence of the lack of natural control on the size of industrial organizations that we once called *farms*.

But a farm is not a machine or a factory. A farm is a living thing. And all living things have a *right* size. Obviously, some elephants are bigger than others, and some mice are smaller than others, but the right size for an elephant is much larger than the right size for a mouse. If a mouse were as big as an elephant, it couldn't survive doing the things that mice do, and if an elephant were as small as a mouse, it couldn't survive doing the things that elephants do. But equally important, a mouse could never live to grow nearly as large as an elephant and an elephant couldn't survive without becoming much larger than a mouse. In nature — in the grand order of things — living things have evolved over time so their size now fits their purpose and function within nature. Living things naturally grow to the right size to do what they need to do.

Unlike plants and animals, however, healthy farms may be different sizes. Unlike natural organisms, farms have neither a predetermined purpose to perform nor a specific set of elements, organs, or resources to be used in carrying out their necessary functions. Thus, farmers must decide what the purpose of their farm is to be and then must organize the resources — the land, labor, capital, and management skills — necessary for the farm to achieve that purpose. In a sense, farmers create their unique farm *organism*. However, all farm organizations still must function according to the basic principles of living organisms. So, each farmer must discover the *right* size necessary to keep his or her farm healthy and the size beyond which it must not be allowed to grow; because if it becomes too large, it cannot survive.

Back in the early 1960s, I had an opportunity to work with a genuine *giant*. His name was Henry Hite. Henry was one of the *gimmicks* we used to lure people to supermarkets to buy our bacon and hams. (I was working for Wilson & Co., meat packers at the time.) Henry billed himself as being eight feet, two inches tall — although the *Guinness Book of World Records* lists him at seven feet, nine-and-a-half inches. He admitted to me that he wasn't actually eight-foot-two, but said he was at least two inches taller than some other fellow who claimed to be eight-foot-even. Regardless, Henry Hite was a tall fellow — a genuine *giant*.

Perhaps the thing that distinguished Henry most among his peers was that he lived to be more than sixty years old. Most *giants* die young — few surviving their thirties. Henry was lucky. All of his abnormal growth came during his teenage years; by age nineteen, he had stopped growing. Most *giants* keep right on growing, until their body becomes so large their vital organs can no longer support their bulk, and they die. For most *giants*, the biological processes that naturally limit the size of the human body fail to function. They continue to grow beyond their *normal* size, their health begins to decline, and eventually, they die. Henry quit growing before he grew too big to live. He pushed the limits of size, but survived.

A farm is no different in concept from other living organisms — plants, animals, or people. It is a complex *organization* of biological organisms within the soil, of plants and animals above the soil, and of the farmer, who cares for the farm and lives from the farm. The health of the farm is dependent upon the health of its various elements, or organs, but also upon the health of the relationships among the various organs that make up the living organism or farm as a whole. And as with all other living organisms, each farm has a healthy size, beyond which its health begins to decline, and a maximum size, beyond which it will become sick and die.

In general, the health of a farm depends on its ecological, social, and economic dimensions. A healthy farm, as with any other living organism, must function in harmony within its ecological niche. The farm organization and the diversity of its enterprises must fit its natural environment and the diversity of its natural resources — its climate, land, and biological environment. A healthy farm also must function in harmony with the people who farm the land and the people affected by the way it is farmed — the farm family, community, and society. And a healthy farm must meet the realistic expectations of those who depend upon the farm for their economic livelihood.

A farm that expands beyond its ecological niche invariably degrades its natural resource base — soil, air, or water — and eventually diminishes its health and productivity. If it persists in trying to function in conflict with nature, the farm will not survive. A farm that expands beyond its social niche invariably creates conflicts within the family, within the community, or within the larger society. If it persists in trying to function in conflict with its social environment, the farm will not survive. However, a farm that fails to expand enough to fulfill its economic purpose without creating ecological or social conflict, likewise, is not a healthy farm. For a farm to be healthy, it must be of a size that allows balance and harmony among its ecological, social, and economic functions. It needs to grow large enough to be productive, but if it becomes too large, it will become sick and die, and thus, will no longer serve any purpose, economic or otherwise.

Eventually, farmers must come to realize that agricultural industrialization is in direct conflict with nature's requirements for agricultural sustainability. And the laws of natural sustainability cannot be changed, even with the most sophisticated of industrial technologies. Farms with a future must be of a natural *right* size; most farms of the future will be smaller.

2004

22 | Farming at the Edge of Order & Chaos

Springtime serves to remind us of the order and chaos in nature. Nothing is more predictable, certain or orderly than is the changing of seasons. Nothing is more unpredictable, uncertain, or chaotic than is the weather during the changing of seasons. Nature thrives at the edge of order and chaos. A farm is a thing of nature. Like a wild animal, a farm may be trained but is never really domesticated. At times, a farm may seem orderly and under control; at other times, it seems chaotic and uncontrollable.

For centuries, farmers have tried to domesticate their farms, to bring the chaos of nature under control. Farmers wanted to free themselves from the wrath of nature — from the frosts, droughts, floods, hailstorms, and windstorms that could destroy their dreams along with their crops. They wanted to control the pests and diseases that frustrate their attempts to grow the specific things that we humans value most, rather than the diverse things that nature would grow instead.

The industrialization of farming — with its mechanization, hired labor, genetic selection, irrigation, agrochemicals, antibiotics and hormones, and more recently, genetic engineering — is the result of farmers' historical struggle to establish control over the chaos of nature. The success of industrial agriculture is seen in ever-fewer farmers producing ever-larger quantities of agricultural commodities for ever-lower dollar and cent prices. However, the failure of industrialization is seen in the ever-growing ecological and social costs, which are not reflected in food prices but borne by society in general. These growing costs reflect the persistent resistance of nature to farmers' attempts to control.

Nature always has the last word. Crops still freeze because weather is still unpredictable. Irrigation aquifers are depleted as farmers try to produce too much in areas with too little rainfall. As higher levies are built along rivers, floodwaters rise higher, and eventually the larger floods break through. Now with global warming, weather is becoming more volatile, and rainstorms, hailstorms, windstorms, freezes, and droughts will become even more severe. Now with biotechnology, we can expect super-weeds and super-insects as nature responds to each new attack. Perhaps even more important are the violations of human nature as people are treated as unfeeling, uncaring cogs in huge industrial machines. By nature, humans fight back against oppression, whether political or economic in nature. Nature is fighting back against industrialization. Nature thrives at the edge of order and chaos and simply refuses to be domesticated.

A growing body of literature from a wide range of scientific disciplines now indicates that the adaptability and long run effectiveness of any system, meaning its sustainability, can be maintained only at the edge of order and chaos. Only living systems are capable of productivity as well as self-renewal and regeneration, and thus, only living systems are capable of sustainability. Sustainability depends on our willingness and ability to accept and embrace the nature of living things. Sustainable farms, being living systems, depend on the willingness and ability of farmers to work and live in harmony with nature — at the edge of order and chaos.

Order, knowing what to do and how to do it, arises from experiences in dealing with the same basic problems and opportunities over an extended time period, regardless of whether we are talking about farmers managing pests, people making public policy, or species evolving to fit their ecological niches. We try things, some seem to work, others don't; and so, we learn to do the things that seem to work best. Farmers tried the new chemical and mechanical technologies, some seemed to work, others didn't; they used the ones that worked and discarded the others.

Order works well, as long as the natural and social environments — the sources of problems and opportunities — don't change too much. We become more effective and efficient as we learn to do things in a more orderly fashion. But, if the environment changes — if we encounter new problems or discover new opportunities — our orderly ways of doing things may no longer be appropriate. We may be very efficient, meaning we do things right, but we may not be effective, meaning we may not do the right things. In addition, orderly processes often become very entrenched and resistant to changes. We know what works, so we aren't going to waste time or money on new, unproven ideas.

Chaos implies an absence of order. In chaos, people go in all different directions and try all sorts of things; there is no common understanding of what they are trying to do or how best to do it. Chaotic farmers try all sorts of things to manage pests, grow crops, and care for livestock with no common understanding of what a farm actually is or what they can expect from it. In a chaotic nature, plants, animals, and insects mutate and migrate into new environments and compete for new ecological niches. In a chaotic society, people address new social, ecological, and economic issues in new political environments, following all sorts of new approaches, without a common understanding of what they want to achieve or how to go about it.

Chaos is very inefficient and is only sporadically effective. It's pretty much a hit-or-miss proposition. But chaos is an essential element of change. Evolution is orderly, but revolution is chaotic. Evolution is capable of finding better ways to do things. Revolution is capable of finding better things to do. In ecological terms, evolution allows organisms to become more efficient by better adapting to their environment while chaos allows organisms to become more effective and allows organisms to find new environments where they can be more efficient and effective. When environments are dramatically altered, survival may well depend upon the capacity for dramatic, chaotic change.

Of course, chaos can lead to failure and extinction. But so can order. Far more nations, people, and ideas die of atrophy than die from revolution. Both order and chaos are necessary ingredients for long run success — for sustainability. Sustainability can persist only at the edge of order and chaos. At the edge of chaos and order, there is sufficient order to ensure a measure of efficiency but also sufficient chaos to accommodate an ever-changing environment of new challenges and opportunities.

Many farmers today, particularly those on small- and medium-sized family farms, seem afraid to abandon the order of conventional, industrial agricultural production, even though the changing environment of agriculture makes their failure virtually certain. Most farms are simply not large enough to compete in today's global economy. Yet farmers persist in producing and marketing the same old commodities in the same old ways because it seems more orderly and efficient to do so. Many farmers are even willing to give up control of their farming operations — through comprehensive, corporate contracts — just so they can continue doing the things with which they have become comfortable. Most farmers today resist the uncertainties of the new sustainable farming systems, such as organic production, specialty crops, niche markets, direct marketing to local customers, or working cooperatively with other farmers to access higher-volume food markets. They don't know how to do these things, and too many things are unpredictable or uncontrollable. These new approaches to farming just seem too chaotic.

The agricultural institutions, including agricultural colleges, state and federal departments of agriculture, and most farm organizations, all suffer this same unwillingness to venture out to the edge of chaos. The scientists, bureaucrats, and advocates cling to the false hopes that new biological technologies, information technologies, or global opportunities will somehow allow them to gain control over nature. After all, they have succeeded, academically and economically, by focusing on doing the same things better. Why should they risk failure now by searching for new and better things to do? The politicians and lobbyists try to create the illusion that fine-tuning failed policies from the past will create successful policies for the future. They have spent many years developing constituencies and political support for an evolutionary approach to public policy. Why should they risk revolution by putting forth new policies that actually might work? Those in positions of power gained their power doing what they have been doing. They are unwilling to risk venturing out to the edge of chaos.

Those farmers who are waiting for things to settle down and become orderly before they venture out onto the frontier of sustainable agriculture will be waiting forever. There is order in sustainable agriculture, but the order is within the chaos. Sustainable farmers must work in harmony with nature, and nature is both orderly and chaotic.

When sustainable farmers lose a crop to drought, flood, or frost, they change fields, planting dates, crop rotations, or even change crops. They do what they must to accommodate the nature of their particular farm. When the organic foods market was captured by large, industrial producers, many farmers moved beyond organic to market sustainably grown, local foods. When consumers became concerned about the use of growth hormones, antibiotics, and other confinement livestock feeding practices, sustainable farmers respond with humanely raised, hormone and antibiotic free meats. When sustainable farmers outgrow farmers' markets, they start CSAs or begin marketing their best products to local chefs. When

CSAs become too large and burdensome, sustainable farmers form multi-farm CSAs, start on-line buying clubs, or form cooperatives to gain access to higher-volume markets. Sustainable farmers thrive on the edge of order and chaos.

These sustainable farmers are showing the way to the future for the rest of society. To sustain agriculture, to sustain human life on earth, we must all learn to thrive at the edge of order and chaos.

2006

ECONOMICS

23 | The Three Economies of Agriculture

O ur pursuit of narrow, economic self-interests is the root cause of virtually every threat to the sustainability of American agriculture today. To reduce the dollar and cent cost of food production, we have promoted industrial farming methods that have degraded the long-run productivity of the land and polluted the natural environment. Our farms have become larger, our farm families fewer, and our rural communities have suffered because Americans wanted cheaper food. We have exploited both land and people in our pursuit of economic efficiency. If we are to restore sustainability to our food and farming systems, we must pursue a more enlightened concept of economics.

As individuals, our actions need not be motivated solely by our economic self-interest. We know that our lives are made better by positive relationships with other people, regardless of whether such relationships result in anything of economic value. We know that our lives gain meaning and purpose through acts of stewardship, regardless of whether such acts yield anything of economic value. But, to encourage such actions across the larger society, we need an economic system that rewards, rather than penalizes, acts of compassion and of stewardship. At the very least, we need an economic system that does not encourage and reward the exploitation of the very resources, both human and ecological, upon which the future of humanity depends. We need a new economics of sustainability.

The concept of sustainability is far broader than economics — at least the economics of today. John Cobb and Herman Daly, in their book, *For the Common Good,* refer to today's economics as chrematistics — the "manipulation of property and wealth so as to maximize short-term monetary exchange value to the owner." However, the root-word for economics, *oikonomia,* means "management of the household (community, society, humanity, biosphere) so as to increase its value to all members over the long run." Oikonomia includes management of society and ecology as well as the economy and is sufficiently broad to address the concept of sustainability.

An economics of sustainability must be multidimensional — with social and ecological dimensions, as well as the conventional individual dimension. The three dimensions must be considered as interdependent aspects of the same whole, with each making distinctive contributions to a "sustainable economy." Thus, the individual economy, the social economy, and the moral economy are but three aspects of the same economy.

First, the individual economy typically is referred to as the private economy — it's what comes to mind today when someone mentions "economics." The individual or private economy will play an important role in a sustainable society in meeting our needs as individuals. Whenever decisions have little effect, either positive or negative, on anyone other than the decision-maker, such decisions can legitimately be guided by the private or individual economy. A sustainable economy will have a large and legitimate private sector because many decisions are fundamentally individual and private in nature.

However, in order for the private economy to function in the collective interests of society, we must restore competition to the economic marketplace, and this can be done. The corporate monopolies of the early 1900s were brought under control by people working through their government. Once people understood the societal implications of a corporately dominated economy, they rebelled. They started the Progressive Movement, the corporate "trusts were busted," and competition was restored. However, even if private sector markets were functioning perfectly, even if we still had true competitive capitalism, the private economy could not meet all of the needs of society.

Those things most clearly belonging to the social or public economy are things to which all people have equal rights, regardless of their ability to pay. Our Declaration of Independence states, "all people are created equal" and have inalienable rights including "life, liberty, and the pursuit of happiness." This doesn't mean that all must succeed, but all must have an equal opportunity to succeed. The U.S. Constitution confirms this commitment. The purposes for forming the Union include, "to promote the general welfare, and secure the blessings of liberty to ourselves and our posterity," as well as, "to establish justice, insure domestic tranquility, and provide for the common defense." The social economy is the means by which we make decisions for the good of all.

The public economy is not directed by dollars and cents, but instead, is directed by the will of the people. In the private economy, the ability to have more, if you earn more, provides a powerful and necessary motivation for productivity and progress. However, in the public economy, everyone has an equal voice in the decision making process, regardless of income or wealth, since everyone has an equal right to benefit. In the public or social economy, all people are equal, and each person has but one vote, regardless of wealth. Social equality is our only means of building and maintaining positive, productive relationships among people of differing abilities and economic means. The social economy is our only means of encouraging healthy families, communities, and nations.

The social economy includes the legitimate institutions of government, but also includes all of the other private, nonprofit institutions that are committed to building a more civil society. Through the social economy, we make deliberate, purposeful decisions to build each other up so that we may all share a higher quality of life by being part of something greater than our collective individuality.

The third economy, the ecological economy, is directed neither by dollars and cents nor by the vote of people but instead by moral and ethical consensus. Eventually, we must realize that stewardship of the resources of the earth ultimately is a spiritual matter. The natural environment is not a commodity to be bought and sold in the marketplace, nor is it a public good to be negotiated and compromised in the halls of Congress. Future generations cannot compete for resources in the marketplace, nor can they vote in the political process. The natural environment is a sacred trust — a gift that must be conserved and preserved for all generations.

The ecological economy emerges from a process of consensus — the result of a community, national, or global dialog concerning what we people believe to be moral and ethical behavior. Ultimately, the stewardship ethics of people such as John Muir, Aldo Leopold, and Rachel Carson must be folded into a shared vision of our ecological future. Once a consensus is reached, it can be encoded into the constitutions of nations, and into international treaties, with the expressed purpose of ensuring the long-run sustainability of human life on earth. But such a consensus must first be achieved in the hearts and souls of people.

The necessary components of the new sustainable economy already exist. We already have a private economy through which to pursue our individual interests. We need only restore its competitiveness. We have a government through which to pursue our social interests. We need only restore its integrity. And, we have a constitution that could be amended to reflect more fully a national consensus of our ethical and moral values — including an environmental ethic. All we need is a shared vision concerning how the individual economy, the social economy, and the ecological economy should work together to sustain a more desirable quality of human life — and the courage to pursue it.

The three economics of agriculture must be built upon the three economies of sustainability. First, there is a legitimately large private sector of the agricultural economy. No other economic system can approach the efficiency of a free market economy in allocating the use of land, labor, and capital to meet the food and fiber needs of people. A primary downfall of communism was the failure of its centrally planned agriculture to meet the needs of its people. We must restore competition to the agricultural economy if it is to benefit consumers rather than corporate investors. But private markets have no equal in meeting the food and fiber needs of those who are able to pay.

However, a free market economy will not ensure that all people have sufficient food for survival or for physical growth and mental development. Free markets will not protect the land from degradation or the natural environment from pollution. Free markets will not ensure that all who choose to farm will have an equal opportunity to succeed. In summary, the private sector will protect neither land nor people from economic exploitation. Thus, if agriculture is to be sustainable, it must rely on the public as well as the private sector of the agricultural economy.

Government provides the means by which we make public decisions. The fundamental purpose of government programs for agriculture should be to ensure that the important public functions of agriculture are performed — including food equity, food security, environmental protection, and employment opportunity. Private markets provide no incentives to perform these functions, yet they also are critical to our societal well-being.

The intergenerational issues in agriculture, including ecological and cultural stewardship, are ethical and moral issues. Eventually, we must develop a national consensus concerning the rights of future generations. Eventually, the rights of all future generations, including their rights to a healthy environment and to healthy communities, will be encoded in our constitution. Since those of future generations cannot participate in the process of rewriting our constitution, they must depend on the ethical and moral values of those of us who can. In the meantime, the moral economy that must guide both our private and public economies must be encoded in our hearts and our souls.

2002

Rethinking Government Farm Programs from the Ground Up

*T*he U.S. Congress is hard at work writing the 2002 Farm Bill.[1] The last farm bill, the Freedom to Farm Act, was designed to phase out government farm programs. It was supposed to "get the government off the farmers' backs." U.S. farmers were to have been prospering from participation in the new global free market by now. Obviously, the act didn't live up to its early billing. Once farmers were "free to farm," they flooded markets with production, global prices plummeted, and farmers were left "free to fail" instead. Washington has responded year after year with emergency payments for farmers. Instead of being phased out of farm programs, U.S. farmers are now among the most heavily subsidized in the world. It seems a sensible time to rethink the whole concept of government farm programs, from the ground up.

Congress is not inclined to change things too much or too quickly, under any circumstances. And those large farming operations that have been filling their bank accounts at the public trough are lobbying to make the generous emergency bailouts of recent years a permanent part of the new farm bill. I'm sure all farmers appreciate their government checks, but small farmers benefit relatively little from current farm programs. Small farmers hold a very small proportion of total "base acres" for the major crops — corn, soybeans, wheat, cotton, rice, sugar, etc. — on which most current government payments are made. So their government checks are proportionately small. Many small farms don't bother to participate in government programs.

1. This article was written in the fall of 2001 but is just as relevant today.

In addition, as most family farmers have discovered when government payments are raised, commodity prices drop and costs of production rise, leaving them no better off than before. As one of my economist friends puts it, farmers have become the "bagmen" who launder government checks for the corporate agribusiness firms, the ultimate benefactor of surplus production. Large landowners and agribusinesses don't want things to change — at least not too much. So, it will be up to small farmers and taxpayers to demand radical changes in government farm programs.

First, government payments should go to those who produce things that benefit the public in general, but for which the private-market incentives are inadequate or do not exist. There was a time when government programs that helped farmers to increase their efficiency and to bring down food prices provided a legitimate public service. Today, however, farming accounts for less than a dime of each dollar spent for food. In addition, production is increasingly controlled by giant agribusiness corporations. These giant firms pass little, if any, of farm production cost reductions on to food consumers. We can no longer make food cheaper by making farming more efficient. Government farm programs have become "corporate welfare" programs.

Second, farmers are in a position to provide legitimate and valuable *public* benefits to society, and society could benefit greatly from investing *public* dollars to create those benefits. Food security, food equity, environmental protection, and rural communality are but a few of those benefits that farmers could create, but for which private incentives are inadequate or non-existent.

Finally, farmers have a legitimate right to receive employment security benefits such as those provided to other workers through minimum wages, workers' compensation, unemployment benefits, and so on. Similar *public* benefits could be provided to farmers who are willing to produce truly *public* goods and services for society. This would require a rethinking of farm programs. But using public tax dollars to create public goods and services is the legitimate role of government. Subsidizing corporate investors is not.

As Americans, we believe in the words in our Declaration of Independence, "that all men are created equal, that they are endowed by their Creator with certain unalienable Rights, that among these are Life, Liberty and the pursuit of Happiness — that to secure these rights, Governments are instituted among Men, deriving their just powers from the consent of the governed." We don't believe that we can make everyone happy, but we do believe that everyone has an equal right to the pursuit of happiness. This is the most basic and fundamental purpose of our government, to ensure that all people have equal access to those things to which they have equal rights — to provide *public* goods and services.

The private market does not provide things equally to all — even if markets were perfectly competitive and free, which they are not. The markets provide things in relation to our willingness and ability to pay for them. We are not equally capable of being productive, and thus, are not equally able to earn money or equally able to pay. Thus, governments in democratic societies must ensure economic equity by providing those things that all people deserve *equally* but for which many cannot pay.

For example, nearly everyone agrees that all people, regardless of their economic means, have a right to adequate food, clothing, and shelter to survive and grow. Most also agree that everyone has a right to military protection, some level of education, and some means of transportation. This certainly does not exhaust the list of legitimate public services, but there is little disagreement about these. The private sector will not provide these things, at least not equally to all, so we pay for them with our tax dollars, through government programs.

Why shouldn't we use government programs to ensure that every American has some minimum level of food, clothing, and shelter, and simultaneously, provide employment security to those who provide them? Government already provides such things through various food, housing, and income assistance programs. But the government buys the goods and services from corporate suppliers and ends up supplementing the incomes of minimum-wage corporate employees, while subsidizing the farmers and other independent suppliers that the corporations are driving out of business. This doesn't seem to make much sense. Why shouldn't local governments buy to meet local needs directly from local suppliers? Why not provide employment security directly to those who produce the public benefits and cut out the corporate middlemen?

Why shouldn't we use government programs to provide food security for all, and simultaneously, provide employment security to those who provide it? The government has held strategic reserves of various agricultural commodities in the past and we may well need such reserves in the future. With America becoming increasingly reliant on food imports, we could be as vulnerable to "food crises" in the future as we are to "energy crises" today. In the past, the government has purchased commodities through the open market, stored them in commercial facilities, and has ended up subsidizing farmers because large reserves depressed market prices. Why not purchase commodities for locally held strategic reserves of commodities directly from local farmers and reward farmers who provide such reserves with employment security?

A safe, healthy, and productive natural environment is another "right" that many of us believe should be guaranteed "equally to all." The Conservation Security Act, which has been introduced in Congress, proposes to link payments under the new 2002 Farm Bill to soil and water conservation and environmental protection. It is perfectly legitimate to use public tax dollars to provide incentives to protect the environment for the good of the public. I personally have reservations about paying people to do things that they already have an ethical and moral obligation to do. It seems a bit like paying people not to assault or rob other people. However, linking government payments to conservation benefits rather than past production of commodities would certainly be a step in the right direction.

The Europeans are promoting a concept in international trade negotiations that would pay farmers for a variety of public benefits, including contributions of family farms to rural landscapes, rural culture, and stable communities, in addition to environmental protection. They propose to pay farmers for their "multi-functional" contribution to local communities as well as to society in general. This seems to me to be a perfectly sensible approach to using public tax dollars to provide legitimate public goods and services.

Why shouldn't we combine the concepts of farmers as providers of "multi-functional" public benefits with farmers' rights to employment security? Farmers would provide specifically identified public goods and services, as directly and as locally as possible. Food *equity* commodities could come from local farmers and go to local recipients. Food *security* commodities would come from local farmers and go into local storage. Soil conservation and environmental stewardship would be a prerequisite for participation in any government program. Positive economic and ecological impacts would be local, and thus, would be supportive of safe, healthy, prosperous, and sustainable local communities.

Program benefits paid to farmers would be limited to those consistent with employment security — some minimum level of income year-in and year-out, the ability to continue farming for a living, access to affordable health care and disability benefits. Huge government payments to giant agribusiness corporations would become a thing of the past. Benefits would be paid to individual farm families for their individual contributions of public services. Thus, small farmers would be eligible for the same benefits as large farmers; the maximum benefit would be employment security for one individual or one family, regardless of farm size.

In a sense, such a program would treat participating farms as a "public utility" and treat participating farmers as "public workers." But in what sense is this less defensible or desirable than farmers taking government handouts for doing virtually nothing of true public benefit? Farmers would have the right to use production methods of their choice, as long the result was an acceptable "multi-functional" benefit. This is far more freedom than farmers have under most corporate contracting arrangements. And farmers could still produce as much of any commodity as they wanted, for sale in the open markets. But they would receive no government payment beyond employment security. And farmers could choose not to participate.

Sound a bit radical? Perhaps. But such a program would leave farmers with far more "freedom to farm" than did the last Farm Bill.

2001

25 | The Economics of Happiness

ecently, I received an e-mail request from a British publisher to review an Italian economist's proposal to write a book entitled *The History of Happiness in Economics*. Such is the nature of our electronically interconnected world. The proposal included a couple of published papers in which the author, Luigino Bruni, traced the historical development of the discipline of economics. The papers were filled with references, footnotes, and the typical economic jargon, but nonetheless, provided some interesting insights into the past and potential future of farming.

Only within the past century has economics become the *dismal science* — only after abandoning the "pursuit of happiness" for the "pursuit of wealth." Early nineteenth century economists, including notables such as Britain's Adam Smith and Thomas Malthus, considered happiness to be the ultimate goal of all economic activity. Smith wrote of the "wealth of nations," but his writings reflect a clear understanding that one's pursuit of wealth should not take precedent over one's social responsibilities. Malthus, who suggested population ultimately would outstrip our ability to produce food, suggested that Smith assumed too strong a connection between increases in wealth and increases in happiness. Neither assumed that greater wealth was synonymous with greater happiness. In the latter half of the century, the focus of economics shifted toward satisfying individual human "wants," as well as needs, with a clear understanding that human "wants" were affected by human relationships.

However, at the turn of the twentieth century, Vilfredo Pareto, an Italian, set about to free economics from the subjectivity of sociology and psychology, by focusing on the "revealed preferences" rather than happiness. To Pareto, all that mattered was whether a person consistently chose one thing over another. Obviously, rational persons would make choices consistent with their wants and needs. Economists should focus on consumer preferences and choices, he suggested, and let the sociologists and psychologists worry about whether such choices actually make people happier. Pareto's theories eventually were adopted by other economists, primarily because it allowed economics to focus on observable and measurable human behavior, rather than some intangible concept of human happiness.

In the early 1900s, Alfred Marshall, another Brit, conceded that economics no longer dealt directly with human "well-being," his term for happiness, but rather with the "material requisites" of it. Most twentieth-century economists, including England's John Hicks and America's Paul Samuelson, made little distinction between wealth and happiness. They wanted to turn economics into a "hard science," like chemistry and physics. They needed objective, quantifiable economic variables to accommodate their mathematical and statistical models. Maximizing profit, income, or wealth was equivalent to maximizing satisfaction or happiness, as far as they were concerned. Critics questioned the lack of capacity for compassion or altruism in their rational, "economic man." But whatever compassion or altruism the "economic man" might possess, could be reflected in his rational choices, they replied. They ignored the fact that revealed preference theory supported optimum social well-being only if altruism is strictly "impersonal" — showing no preference for one person over another. Thus, the *dismal science* of today was born.

Happiness has always been a matter of discussion and debate among the world's greatest philosophers. It was accepted as the motive of all purposeful human activity. The "hedonist" philosophers equated happiness to sensory pleasures — to individual, personal experiences. Another group of philosophers, including Aristotle, used the term *eudaimonia* for happiness. *Eudaimonia* is inherently social in nature — it is realized by the individual, but only within the context of family, friendships, community, and society. Aristotle's happiness, social happiness, is a natural consequence of positive personal relationships. This social happiness was considered to be a by-product of actions taken for their own sake — not to achieve some sensory satisfaction, but because they are intrinsically good. In essence, Aristotle and his followers believed that happiness was not something to be pursued, but instead, was a natural consequence of "righteous living."

To the extent that contemporary economics includes any remaining element of happiness, it most clearly is *hedonistic* in nature rather than *eudaimonic*. *Eudaimonia* depends on personal relationships, not on some impersonal altruism. Thus, the current pursuit of economic wealth is a pursuit of individual, hedonistic, or selfish sensory pleasure. And pursuit of individual wealth, within this context, inevitably leads to the exploitation of other people and the degradation of human relationships. Thus, the pursuit of individual wealth quite logically has diminished our social happiness.

What hard evidence do we have of this perverse relationship between wealth and happiness? We need only look at trends such as the rising cost of law enforcement and increasing numbers of prisoners, increasing number of lawyers and rising costs of civil litigation, increasing births to unwed mothers, and rising poverty in single-parent households. All of these trends are symptoms of increasingly dysfunctional human relationships and declining social happiness, and all have occurred during a time of rising national wealth.

Robert Putnam, a Harvard political scientist, clearly documents our growing social disconnectedness in his book, *Bowling Alone.* He evaluates a multitude of measures of social involvement, ranging from voting in elections, to belonging to civic and professional organizations, to joining bowling leagues, to visiting friends and neighbors. He concludes that Americans are only about 30 to 50 percent as socially connected today as we were in the late 1950s.

As Aristotle might have predicted, our growing disconnectedness occurred as America was abandoning all social and moral constraints to pursue individual wealth, while the government was promoting maximum economic growth. During the early part of the twentieth century, Americans tempered their economic ambitions with concern for their fellow citizens. They restrained corporate greed at the turn of the century by supporting strong antitrust legislation. They supported Roosevelt's New Deal programs to care for the needy and help lift the nation out of recession. Most supported the Civil Rights movement of the 1960s. But, since the 1960s, there has been little societal or political restraint to the unbridled pursuit of individual economic self-interests.

Aristotle might also have predicted the consequences for our national happiness. Putnam points out that the rate of mental depression among the last two generations of Americans has increased roughly "tenfold" — these being the generations most socially disconnected — over mental depression in the 1950s. Also, between 1950 and 1995, the rate of suicide among American adolescents more than "quadrupled" and among young adults nearly "tripled." Less serious, but no less significant, incidents of "malaise" — headaches, indigestion, and sleeplessness show patterns similar to suicide and mental illnesses. Between the late 1970s and late 1990s, surveys indicate that each new generation, on average, is "unhappier" than the previous generation. In short, as each generation has become increasingly disconnected, the nation as a whole has become increasingly mentally ill and physically miserable. As we have become a nation of greater wealth, we have become a nation of growing unhappiness.

In farming, the pursuit of wealth is seen in a relentless trend toward larger, more specialized, farming operations as farmers are encouraged to give priority to productivity and profitability — to farm for the bottom line. The bottom line has encouraged farms to grow larger, which is possible only by farmers acquiring land from their neighbors. Thus, some farmers had to fail so others might succeed; meaning farmers had to hope, perhaps subconsciously, that their neighbors would be the ones to fail because they would need their neighbor's land to survive. Such hopes are hardly conducive to building strong relationships among neighbors. As families have been forced out of farming, they have left many rural communities in decline and decay, without enough people to support local schools, churches, health care facilities, or main street businesses.

The pursuit of unbridled economic self-interest has turned farms into "factories," pitting neighbor against neighbor. For example, producers and community leaders, expecting profits and tax revenue from large-scale confinement animal feeding operations, are confronted by community members who live downwind or downstream, who suffer from the inevitable pollution of air and water. The social fabric of many rural communities has been split apart by such conflicts. Eventually, the corporate operations will leave these communities, when profit prospects look better elsewhere, leaving a splintered community with the mess to clean up.

Some may argue that this pursuit of wealth has actually brought greater happiness to rural America. But ask them where they expect their children to live. Ask farmers if they even want their children to be farmers. Ask rural residents how many of the "best and brightest" — as they call young people with opportunities elsewhere — will choose to stay or return to the communities where they grew up. Rural people want their children to be happy, so they encourage those who have a choice to live elsewhere.

So, how are we to find happiness? First, we must have the courage to challenge conventional economic thinking that "pursuit of wealth" means "pursuit of happiness." Perhaps, as Marshall said, economics is best viewed as being about acquiring some of the "material requisites" for happiness, but it is not about happiness. Next, we must realize that happiness, in any sense other than hedonistic sensory pleasure, depends on the quality of our personal relationships. Finally, we must understand that happiness is a by-product of "right living" — not something that we pursue, but instead something that comes to us.

What does this have to do with sustainable farming? Everything. Sustainable farming is not about becoming wealthy but instead is about living a good life. As farmers find ways to make a decent living while caring for the land and caring for other people, not only are they building a sustainable agriculture for the future, they are opening the doors to happiness.

2003

Sustainable Farm Policy: Too Much Order, Too Little Chaos

*I*n the summer of 2003, I agreed to participate in a five-month Policy Roundtable discussion of sustainable agriculture policy, coordinated by the national Campaign for Sustainable Agriculture. I agreed only reluctantly because I have always found public policy to be frustrating — too much politics and too little democracy. The policy dialogue, which was carried out mostly through the Internet and conference calls, culminated in a face-to-face meeting in Washington, D.C. in late October. While I learned much from the process, I found the Policy Roundtable experience to be even more frustrating than I had feared.

One reason I agreed to become involved in the process was that I felt there had been a major disconnect between the *grassroots* sustainable agriculture folks who I meet all around the country and sustainable agriculture policy initiatives in Washington, D.C. I just don't find many people at the *grassroots* of the sustainable agriculture movement, either farmers or eaters, who feel they have benefited from past farm policies. The only exceptions I find are those who have received the few dollars that have trickled through into various producer grant programs or have been lucky enough to connect with the small but dedicated core of public servants who are committed, with little institutional encouragement or reward, to working on sustainable agriculture issues. Unfortunately, the Roundtable failed to address this policy disconnect in any meaningful way.

With fundamental redirection, I believe public policy efforts related to sustainable agriculture could yield far greater positive results than we have seen in the past. I think we ultimately must go to the general public, to all those who eat and pay taxes, to find the political support necessary to shift the focus of agricultural policy from economic efficiency and corporate profitability to long run food security through sustainable family farms. We will have a difficult time reaching the public with a clear message of sustainability until we have a clearly stated purpose and set of guiding principles to communicate what the movement is about. However, the Roundtable group steadfastly declined to commit itself to a specific purpose or set of principles — even to a process that might ultimately lead to defining the purpose and principles of sustainable agriculture policy.

Members of the Roundtable included representatives of more than thirty policy-oriented organizations and public institutions from all across the country. While the members of this group may not speak for the sustainable agriculture movement in total, it most certainly speaks for the core advocates of sustainable agriculture policy. Unfortunately, they speak with voices that offer little hope for significant support from Washington for independent family farmers in their efforts to develop a more sustainable American agriculture.

In reflecting on the roundtable process, I concluded that sustainable agriculture policy is suffering from *too much order and too little chaos*. As I have written in a previous *Small Farm Today* article referring to farming, a growing body of literature from a wide range of disciplines indicates that maximum adaptability and long run sustainability of any organization is achieved at the *edge of order and chaos*. Order is the result of knowing the best way to do things and comes from experience in dealing with the same basic problems and opportunities over an extended time period. The nature of order is the same whether we are talking about species evolving to fit their ecological niches, farmers managing pests, or policy makers formulating public policy. By trying different things, we learn what works best.

Order is good, as long as the problems and opportunities don't change too much. We become more efficient as we learn to do things in a more orderly fashion. But when confronted with different problems or opportunities, our "orderly" ways of doing things may no longer be appropriate. We may still be very *efficient,* meaning we do things right, but we may no longer be *effective,* meaning we may not do the right things. However, we may be very reluctant to change. Since we *know what works,* we are reluctant to waste our time or money trying some *off the wall* idea.

Chaos implies an absence of order. In chaos, people go in all different directions and try all sorts of things with no common understanding of what they are trying to do or how to do it. Farmers may try all sorts of things to manage pests, grow crops, and care for livestock with no common understanding of what they are trying to do or how to do it. Policy makers may tackle new social, ecological, and economic issues, with all sorts of new approaches, without a common understanding of what they want to achieve or how to go about it. In chaos, no idea is considered *off the wall* because no one knows what will or won't work.

Chaos is very inefficient and only occasionally effective. But chaos is an essential aspect of fundamental change — of revolution. Evolution is orderly, but revolution is chaotic. Evolution is capable of leading to better ways to do things. Revolution is capable of leading to better things to do. In ecological terms, evolution is necessary for adapting to a given environment while chaos is necessary for adapting to new environments. And whenever the environment is radically altered, survival may well depend on the capacity for radical, chaotic change.

Chaos also can lead to failure but so can order. Far more nations, farms, people, and ideas die from narrow-mindedness than die from radical new ideas. Both order and chaos are necessary ingredients of sustainability. Sustainability is maintained at the *edge of order and chaos* — where there is enough order to ensure a measure of efficiency but also enough chaos to accommodate an ever-changing environment of obstacles and opportunities.

In developing public policy for sustainable agriculture, I believe we have moved too far toward order and too far away from chaos. The sustainable agriculture movement was in chaos during much of the 1980s and early 1990s. Many intelligent, creative, hard-working, *good,* people were pursuing lots of different ideas and new policy initiatives. Some seemed to work, others obviously didn't. During the mid 1990s, there was an implicit, if not explicit, effort to add more order to the policy process. We wanted the process to work more efficiently. We wanted everyone to "sing from the same hymnbook, preferably from the same page." The USDA organic certification program was but one highly visible result of a movement that was getting better organized. And in many respects, the efforts to bring more order out of the chaos were successful in bringing about increased political support for the causes of sustainable agriculture.

However, the policy environment has changed — dramatically. The neoconservatives of the current administration in D.C. are opposing, watering down, or dismantling any program that attempts to address ecological or social issues through government policy. The sustainable agriculture movement has changed. The greatest challenge for farmers today is not learning how to farm sustainably, but instead learning how to connect with sustainability-minded consumers. Federal budget constraints have changed — creating both obstacles and opportunities. Dismantling the agricultural commodity programs would not only reduce the federal budget deficit but also would remove huge subsidies to agricultural industrialization, and at the same time, would make adequate funds available to support the transition to a more sustainable agriculture.

However, these issues cannot be addressed effectively within the order of the existing sustainable agriculture policy arena. We must be willing to risk a period of chaos if we are to address the new challenges and opportunities of sustainable agriculture. Our resources, time, and money are not unlimited, thus efficiency is not irrelevant. So, we must retain a measure of order. Today, however, the movement has too much order and too little chaos to allow for the changes necessary for success in a radically different political environment.

Organizations at the edge of chaos must operate by purpose and principles, not by rules and regulations. The people in such organizations must share a common understanding of what the organization is trying to do, its purpose, and its set of essential guiding principles, which must be followed if the purpose is to be achieved. Through a common commitment to purpose and principles, individuals within the organization are provided with the widest possible latitude in pursuing new ideas and initiatives for the betterment of the organization.

I had hoped the Policy Roundtable could provide an invaluable benefit to the sustainable agriculture movement by at least beginning the process of reaching consensus on the purpose of sustainable agricultural policy and a set of essential guiding principles. With a clear purpose and a set of guiding principles, individuals and organizations would then be free to work on the edge of chaos in redefining and redirecting agricultural policy toward true agricultural sustainability. Policy advocates would be free to expand into whatever policy arenas and work with whatever partners were deemed necessary to meet the needs of people at the grassroots of the sustainable agriculture movement. Unfortunately, my hopes were not realized — at least not yet.

2004

Exporting American Agriculture: Why Economists Don't Care

*I*n this election year, we will be hearing a lot about the *exporting* of American jobs to lower-wage countries. However, this debate could just as easily be framed in terms of the *exporting* of American agriculture. For well over a decade, American agribusiness has been supporting the rapid expansion of agriculture in countries with lower land and labor costs. Brazil is but the most prominent example of this global trend. The USDA reports that Brazil has increased its production of cotton, soybeans, broilers, pork, corn, and beef since the late 1990s by percentages ranging from 25 to 75 percent. And much of the expansion in Brazilian agriculture is supported by American corporate investments.

Strong agricultural markets in 2003 only served to mask this deeper fundamental problem. Keith Collins, Chief Economist for USDA, recently warned, "While I am portraying a positive economic picture for U.S. production agriculture in 2004, that optimism should be tempered by potential consequences of the continued production growth of Brazil and other emerging competitors." Economists understand what is happening to American agriculture. Unfortunately, whether it's exporting American jobs or exporting American agriculture, most economists don't seem to care.

To economists it is a just a matter of corporations minimizing their costs by moving operations to places where farmland is cheaper, and people are willing to work harder for less money. American consumers will benefit from lower cost food, and workers in other countries benefit from new employment opportunities. Displaced American farmers will have to find other employment, doing something in which they can compete in the global labor market. Higher returns for American farmers in the past have resulted from protectionism, not higher productivity, and removing this protection will result in a more efficient allocation of land, labor, and capital. Higher profits for corporate investors will more than offset losses in U.S. farm income, leaving the American economy stronger than before.

There is nothing inherently wrong with this argument if economists would just leave it there, or better yet, would go on to explain the inherent limitations of contemporary economic thinking. Economics today simply does not deal with issues of social equity or justice. Economists do not consider the social consequences of destroying a person's occupation, of changing their social status within their family, their community, their society, or of diminishing or destroying their self-esteem. Especially in farming, a person's occupation may largely define their sense of self.

Economics simply doesn't deal with the value of social relationships, which economists call "interpersonal utility." To economists, a society is simply a collection of individuals; an economic whole is nothing more than the sum of its individual parts. With respect to exporting American agriculture, if the winners, in this case investors, could conceivably compensate the losers, in this case farmers, and have something left, the economy is said to be stronger. Never mind that dollars cannot compensate for the degradation of human relationships or that the winners never actually compensate the losers. To economists, if the economy is bigger the economy is better, regardless of the consequences for social equity.

In addition, economics doesn't deal with ethics — with questions of justice, of right and wrong. Economists take consumers' "tastes and preferences" as "given" and boast of making no judgment regarding whether individual "wants" are good or bad for a society. However, economics attempts to allocate the resources of the earth, both human and natural, to satisfying those "wants" as if they were inherently right and good.

Economists ignore the fact that corporations spend billions of dollars for persuasive advertising, targeted to bending, twisting, and shaping consumers' tastes and preferences in order to enhance profits and economic growth. They also conveniently ignore widespread exploitation of workers and consumers, by assuming that all consumers and workers have the freedom and equal opportunity of choosing among a wide range of alternative product and employment options. Economists also ignore the inevitable moral consequences of a dominant global culture that glorifies the pursuit of individual greed. Economics has its own special non-ethic.

As explained in a previous article, the discipline of economics abandoned the social and ethical principles of "classical economic" philosophy in the early 1900s, in developing today's "neoclassical economics." Since then, economics has not dealt directly with human "well-being," but instead, at the very most, with the "material requisites" of well-being. In fact, most economists today make very little distinction between wealth and well-being. In economics, maximizing profit, income, or wealth is essentially equivalent to maximizing satisfaction, well-being, or happiness.

What economists "just don't get," or perhaps won't admit, is they are using "classical" economic philosophy to defend "neoclassical" economic strategies. Classical economist, Adam Smith, in his *Wealth of Nations* wrote that the individual trader "intends only his own gain, . . . but is led by an *invisible hand* to promote . . . that of society more effectually than when he really intends to promote it." As he explained, the validity of this assertion depended on investors naturally "preferring the support of domestic to that of foreign investment." Smith was clearly concerned with the ethical implications of a person choosing to invest in a nation other than his or her own.

David Ricardo, another classical economist, explained that when two individuals choose to trade, each is better off after the trade than before. He observed that each of us values the same things somewhat differently. So, if I value something that you now own more highly than I value something I own, and you value the thing that I own more highly than you value the thing you own, we will both gain by trading. I will get something that I value more than the thing I now own and so will you.

Others have used these same concepts to show the potential gains from trade associated with economic specialization among nations. For example, if the workers of one nation are more efficient wheat producers and workers in another are more efficient producers of computers, then one country can specialize in wheat and the other in computers. The better wheat producers can then trade wheat for computers, and the better computer producers can trade computers for wheat; they both will be better off than if each tried to produce both wheat and computers. Ricardo also pointed out that even those who are less efficient than the others in producing both items will be relatively less inefficient in producing one than in the other, and thus will have a "comparative advantage" in producing the one for which they are less inefficient.

However, both Smith's and Ricardo's observations applied to the world about which they were writing — the world of 200 years ago. None of the conditions necessary for Smith's *invisible hand* to transform the pursuit of short run self-interest into societal good exists today. Today's markets are not competitive, at least not in the classical economic sense. There are not "many" buyers and sellers, it is not easy to "enter or exit" an industry, market participants do not have "perfect information," and consumers are not "sovereigns." Admittedly, the economy of today produces "lots of cheap stuff," but economic theory provides no assurance that it is producing the "right stuff."

International trade among nations today is not comparable to barter between two independent individuals. In order to have free trade, each trading partner must be "free to not trade." In free trade, one partner cannot be dominated by or dependent upon the other — each partner must have other feasible alternatives. In free trade, both parties must have adequate and equal information regarding the ultimate consequences of the trade. Free trade cannot be linked to or conditioned by such things as debts, threats, or defense agreements.

Perhaps most important, trade among nations of people is fundamentally different from trade among individuals. For the individual, the person, the whole being, can decide if he or she will be better off or worse off after a trade. Nations have no easy means of determining whether the *whole* of society is better or worse off, with inevitable winners and losers and no objective way of measuring economic equity or justice.

Investing has important ethical and moral implications. When one nation invests or hires workers in another nation, it is analogous to buying a part of another person — more like slavery than employment. When a sector of the domestic economy is abandoned by its investors, it's like having some part of one's self sold to another — it's a betrayal. Even if both economies are made stronger, both societies may be left weaker.

The world of economics is a purely logical and rational world. In such a world, economic security is equivalent to national security. A wealthy nation would never go to war against a poor nation to ensure access to its oil. A wealthy nation would have no reason for concern in depending on a poor nation for its food. Obviously, we do not live in this rational, logical world of economics.

Smith and Ricardo would roll over in their graves if they knew how their economic philosophies were being misused by economists to justify the exploitation of people and of nature. Every nation has a right and a responsibility to protect its people and its resources from exploitation, regardless of the economic incentives to do otherwise. Only when these rights of individuals, of every nation, are ensured will free trade and the free flow of capital result in stronger societies. Growing opposition to the "exporting of American agriculture," has its logical roots in these fundamental social and ethical principles. But, economics has no social or ethical conscience. That's why most economists don't seem to care.

2004

MARKETS

28 | The New American Food Culture

"Eating is a moral act," as my friend Brother David Andrews, a fellow promoter of sustainable agriculture, is fond of saying. Although we may not give it much thought, what we choose to eat is a reflection of our basic values and beliefs. Eating makes a social statement — we eat with our family and our friends. Eating makes a political statement – what we eat affects what other people will and won't have to eat. Eating makes a moral statement — what we eat affects how the earth is treated, and thus, reflects our personal ethics. Whether we think about it or not, eating is a reflection of our character, our politics, and our culture.

For the most part, Americans want their food to be quick, convenient, and cheap — regardless of whether they buy it at a supermarket or a local fast-food franchise. Americans like things that are fast and easy, requiring minimal personal or economic sacrifice. Americans also value "looking good" and choose foods that "look good." Some are even willing to spend a lot of money for food that makes *them* look good — as when they eat in expensive restaurants. The characteristics of America's dominant food culture are cost, convenience, and appearance.

However, a new American food ethic is emerging to challenge these dominant values. The rapid growth in demand for organic foods, averaging more than 20 percent per year for more than a decade, is but one among several indicators of a new food ethic. Organic foods were neither cheaper nor more attractive than conventional food, nor were they more convenient to acquire. The early organic consumers were more likely to be labeled "counter-cultural" than as "trend setters." Those who chose organic foods obviously were expressing a different food ethic.

Farmers' markets, community supported agriculture organizations (CSAs), and other means of direct food marketing have experienced growth rates similar to those for organic foods. So, the new food ethic cannot be defined simply as an aversion to agricultural chemicals or genetic engineering. The new American food ethic reflects a desire to build relationships with farmers, and through farmers, with the earth. Certainly, some organic consumers are concerned mainly, if not exclusively, with their own physical well-being. But, many others buy organic foods because the philosophical roots of organics are in stewardship and community, in caring for the earth and its people. Most who buy food at farmers markets, CSAs, and other direct marketing venues seek out farmers who share this new and different American food ethic, regardless of·whether their products are certified as organic.

The new food culture might seem insignificant, if we look only at sales of "alternative" food products — including, organic, natural, pesticide free, hormone and antibiotic free, free range, grass-fed, and so on. Sales of such products probably amount to only three or four percent of total food sales — not including foods labeled natural, light, healthy, and so on, that are no different in substance from conventional foods.

But a growing number of Americans are expressing doubts and outright dissatisfaction with the current American food system. And their dissatisfaction is not with cost, convenience, or appearance. They simply don't trust the corporate food manufacturers and distributors, or the government, to ensure the safety and nutritional value of their food. And they certainly don't trust the corporations or government to promote stewardship of land and/or the well-being of ordinary people. These Americans are searching for foods that will reflect a different set of ethical values, not just in the food itself, but in how their food is produced and who benefits and/or suffers as a consequence of its production.

This new *food* culture is but one dimension of a whole new American culture. In their new book, *The Cultural Creatives,* Paul Ray and Sherry Anderson provide compelling evidence that some fifty million Americans are now leading the way in creating this new American culture. The authors identify three distinct groups within American society based on some 100,000 responses to surveys concerning basic values and lifestyles, supplemented by numerous focus groups and personal interviews.

One group, identify as the "cultural creatives," is growing rapidly, and while still a minority, already makes up more than one-quarter of the American adult population. The dominant group, the "moderns," makes up about half of American society. However, only about half of this group is firmly committed to the dominant American culture of materialistic, economic self-interest. About a quarter of those in the "moderns" group are too busy trying to get ahead or to make ends meet to think about what they believe. Those in the remaining quarter actually feel alienated by modern society; it isn't working for them, but they go along because they don't see a viable alternative. The final group, the "traditionalists," makes up about a quarter of the adult population. The authors describe the traditionalists as wanting the world to be "like it used to be but never was."

The core moderns, although no larger in number than the cultural creatives, tend to define American culture because they are disproportionately in positions of economic and political power. The values of the moderns are reflected in our apparent national obsession with material success — making money, getting ahead, looking good, and living an affluent lifestyle. The moderns care about family, community, and have some concern for the natural environment, but they care far more about their individual material success. The traditionalists have strong religious beliefs and hold traditional family values, but they are less concerned about the natural environment than either of the other groups.

The cultural creatives are distinguished from the other two by their strong beliefs in the value of personal relationships, within families, communities, and society as a whole, and by their concern for the integrity and sustainability of the natural environment. They are associated with various movements, including social justice, environmental protection, civil rights, gender rights, and sustainable development. They are less materialistic than either of the other groups and tend to be more spiritual — in the sense of believing in something higher, beyond self.

The values and lifestyles of the cultural creatives are completely consistent with the principles of sustainable development and sustainable agriculture. They believe that quality of life results from equitably meeting the needs of the present while leaving equal or better opportunities for the future. The sustainability movement arose from a growing realization that economic development alone does not increase overall quality of life, but instead, often leads to its degradation. To be sustainable over time, development activities must be ecologically sound, economically viable, and socially responsible. But equally important, balance and harmony among the ecological, economic, and social dimensions of life result in a higher quality of life.

Thankfully, the ranks of the cultural creatives include thousands of new American farmers. These "cultural creating" farmers may call themselves organic, biodynamic, alternative, holistic, natural, ecological, practical, or nothing at all; however, they all fit under the "conceptual umbrella" of sustainable agriculture. The sustainable agriculture movement is a small but critical part of the much larger movement that is creating a new American culture.

The sustainable agriculture movement emerged in response to growing concerns about the sustainability of our corporately controlled, industrial food system. Independent food processors, distributors, and marketers now face the same kinds of challenges, and thus, have the same kinds of opportunities as independent family farmers. Independent food marketers cannot expect to compete with the giant global food chain clusters of today — they have too little market power. If there is to be a future for independent food processors, distributors, or marketers, they must join with sustainable farmers, working and living by a new code of ethics to meet the needs of the new American culture.

The Hartman Report — a respected survey of United States households — identified two consumer groups, the "true naturals" and "new green mainstream," which already make up about twenty-eight percent of the population, as prime markets for sustainably produced foods. These groups are very similar in attitudes and magnitude to Ray and Anderson's "cultural creatives."

Organizations such as the Chefs Collaborative, made up of chefs from up-scale restaurants throughout the country, are helping to create this new culture. Their organizational principles include, "sound food choices emphasizing locally grown, seasonally fresh, and whole or minimally processed ingredients." Their other principles are very much in harmony with the development and support of an ecologically sound and socially responsible food system.

The Slow Food movement is a worldwide organization of "food eaters." It is committed to promoting the diversity of local and regional quality food produced and marketed in ways that guarantees farmers a fair price and protects the environment and the natural landscape. Those in the movement have a clear understanding of the industrial food system, and they realize that a return to local and regional food systems will be necessary for ecological and social sustainability. Slow food is not an elitist gourmet movement, but instead, encourages "good, honest food at reasonable prices" and its appreciation and enjoyment to the fullest by all.

The cultural creatives didn't exist forty years ago and probably accounted for less than ten percent of Americans a decade ago; today they account for more than a quarter of the total population, and their numbers are still growing. Farmers today are serving less than a fifth of this "new American food market." Slowly but surely, a new American food system is being developed by a coalition of sustainable farmers, marketers, and like-minded eaters. Together, these farmers, marketers, and citizen eaters are creating the new American food culture.

2003

Restoring Integrity to the Food System

G rowing consumer distrust of the industrial food system is creating new opportunities for small farmers in higher-volume retail food markets. More and more consumers are becoming concerned about the safety, wholesomeness, and nutritional value of food offered in supermarkets and fast food restaurants. Their concerns are not limited to safety and quality; they are also concerned about the mistreatment of farm animals, farm workers, farmers, and the land. Increasingly, consumers want to know where their food came from, how it was produced, and who produced it. They want a relationship with their farmers. This new consumer-driven movement represents new hope for greater economic success for small farms.

As independent food processors and retailers realize they are facing the same threats from corporate consolidation as those faced by independent family farms, they are becoming more open to forming alliances with farmers. Independent farmers, processors, and retailers working in cooperation have the ability to create a new alternative food system, reconnecting eaters with farmers, and through farmers, with the earth. These new food alliances can provide more sustainably produced food to more caring customers, while creating new opportunities for more small farms.

Farmers' markets, CSAs, roadside stands, and other face-to-face markets will continue to be important to most small farms. But retail food stores and restaurants are the new marketing frontier of sustainable agriculture. The critical challenge in accessing these high-volume markets is to maintain the integrity of the system, not just the integrity of food quality and safety, but also, integrity of relationships — among eaters, retailers, processors, farmers, and through farmers, with the land. Small farm operations have a unique advantage in meeting this challenge because they require fewer customers, making meaningful relationships both possible and more likely. But simply having an advantage does not imply that the task will be easy.

The temptation of falling back into the old impersonal mass-production, mass-marketing mindset becomes stronger as market connections become more numerous, less direct, and less personal. Those who succeed in resisting the temptation must have a firm commitment to the principles of sustainability — to ecological and social integrity as a means of maintaining economic viability. Sustainable systems must be built upon relationships of integrity, regardless of whether relationships are face-to-face or are once or twice removed. Once that integrity is compromised, the system loses its sustainability.

Another challenge for small farmers in accessing higher-volume markets is that of working together for their mutual benefit. Individually, small farmers are simply not capable of providing the volume and variety of consistent high-quality products needed to supply even a small supermarket chain, a large restaurant, or a school. Only by planning their production together and pooling their products for processing and marketing, can small farmers successfully access and benefit from these bigger marketing opportunities. Regardless of whether farmers form a farmers cooperative or some other form of business organization, they must learn to work together if they are to succeed. They must see the wisdom of benefiting collectively as a means of benefiting individually, rather than trying to benefit individually as a means of benefiting collectively.

Typically, the initial purpose for cooperation is to realize economic benefits. However, a cooperative venture among farmers cannot be sustained if it is viewed simply as a business venture. At some point, members inevitably will be confronted with opportunities to realize greater short run benefits by doing things contrary to the long run collective interest of the organization. The most common example, an outside buyer will offer higher prices to individual members than the cooperative is capable of paying to its members. If individual members abandon the cooperative venture in order to realize greater individual benefits in the short run, they inevitably will destroy the ability of the organization to provide them with greater benefits collectively, and individually, over the long run. Buyers with no commitment to the principles of sustainability may intentionally devise strategies to break the collective will of cooperative organizations so they can deal with members individually. During such times, the only thing that holds the collective together are the personal commitments of the members to each other — for social and ethical reasons, as well as for their long run, economic well-being.

Unfortunately, few farmers learn the art and science of commitment and relationships, either during their upbringing or as part of their professional development. Americans, in general, are taught to be independent and self-sufficient, to rely on themselves rather than relate to or commit to others. Men, in particular, may reach adulthood with little understanding of how to build or maintain personal relationships and with little real comprehension of the value of doing so. Relationships are important to the success of farmers who market through farmers markets, CSAs, and roadside stands, but relationships are absolutely essential in creating and sustaining the cooperative ventures needed to access higher-volume markets.

Business education typically focuses on strategies and techniques of personnel management and customer relations, rather than on building personal relationships. However, sustainable relationships must be based on trust and caring, rather than strategy or technique. If a marketing strategy, for example, relies on techniques that mislead or manipulate customers, the deception ultimately will be discovered and the relationship will be lost. If it lacks trust and caring, it lacks sustainability.

Sustainable relationships must be based on principles rather than techniques. Steven Covey, in his book, *The 7 Habits of Highly Effective People,* addresses principle-based relationships, perhaps as well as anyone who has written on the subject. Covey writes, "natural laws in the human dimension . . . are just as real, just as unchanging, and arguably 'there' as laws such as gravity in the physical dimension." Principles are different from values, in that values reflect the conventional wisdoms that are passed on from one generation to the next, and thus may change over time and be different among different cultures. Covey points out that even gangs of thieves have values, they just don't happen to be values that are acceptable to civil society.

Principles come from our common sense of right and wrong — the things we know to be true and good because we sense it in the very core of our being. This common sense comes to us all quite naturally, regardless of our native intelligence, our social status or background, or our training and education. Some people choose to ignore their common sense, relying instead on the conventional wisdom of others or things they have learned through experimentation and observation. But we all have access to the fundamental principles of positive relationships if we are willing to listen to our common sense.

Covey's seven habits of effectiveness are based on principles. His first three habits address individual effectiveness, including setting goals, setting priorities, and being proactive. These habits lead from dependence to independence. The next three address collective effectiveness, or relationships, and include thinking win/win, seeking first to understand and then to be understood, and working for synergy — where the total is greater than the sum of the parts. These allow the individual to move beyond independence to achieve *interdependence,* to develop relationships of mutual benefit.

Some may argue that people will never reach agreement on matters of principle. However, such arguments mistake values for principles. People disagree concerning values, but not core principles. For example, the Institute for Global Ethics has questioned people of many different cultures, religions, and nationalities in many countries of the world regarding ethical principles. They have found that people of all cultures, religions, and nationalities agree on several moral or ethical principles although they disagree widely on values.

The Institute lists five ethical principles of which people hold a common sense of their rightness. They are honesty, fairness, responsibility, compassion, and respect. Who among all of civilized society believes it to be right and good to be dishonest, unfair, irresponsible, unkind, and disrespectful? These core principles could go a long way toward ensuring the sustainability of any relationship or any organization, including a farmers' cooperative.

If farmers are to be successful in their efforts to work together to access higher-volume markets, they will do well to begin with a firm commitment to each other and to their customers, to treat each other with honesty, fairness, responsibility, compassion, and respect. They can then work with traditional cooperative and business development professionals to develop their statements of purpose or goals and to develop an organizational structure and business strategies for carrying out their purpose or achieving their goals. However, they should reject any goal, structure, or strategy that conflicts with these fundamental ethical principles. No organization can be sustained if there is lack of trust among its members.

Finally, it is far easier to sustain a cooperative venture, or any other type of relationship, if we are working with or for people that we like. We need to either work with friends and work for friends or make friends with those with whom and for whom we work. It's simply very difficult to maintain a positive business relationship with someone that you don't like personally. So our sustainable organizations need to become communities of personal interest and personal commitment, not communities of economic interest and contractual commitments. Economic interest and contractual commitments inherently create stress and ultimately destroy personal relationships. Only when we give equal priority to friendship and ethical relationships can we sustain economic relationships. Sustainability depends on harmony and balance among the social, ethical, and economic.

2005

30 | Anyone Can Afford Good Food

Perhaps people who have money can eat like that, but what about poor people?" I hear comments such as this in nearly every discussion of the growing opportunities for people to eat more locally grown, sustainably produced foods. My typical response is that just about anyone anywhere can find good locally grown food these days, and just about anyone can afford it.

Locally grown foods, particularly meat, milk, and eggs, are probably going to cost a good bit more than comparable items in the supermarkets. But most people, even those with modest incomes, can afford to buy good local foods, simply by spending a bit less on other things that add less to their health and happiness. As I have written before, costs of good local foods tend to be higher because local sustainable producers pay the full cost of production; they don't pollute the environment or exploit other people in the production process. Once people understand the differences between typical industrial-produced foods and local sustainably produced foods — in terms of freshness, flavor, wholesomeness, and nutrition, as well as social and ethical integrity — good local food acquires a priority that makes it more easily affordable.

The average American family spends only about a dime out of each dollar of disposable income for food. So, spending ten or even twenty percent more for *good* food only requires spending one or two percent more of the typical family's income for food, rather than for some other discretionary budget item. In some cases, good food may not require actually giving up anything else. For example, the average American family today spends about fifteen percent of their income for health care, and as we learn more about the linkages of diet with health, it's becoming evident that spending a bit more for good food could result in spending a lot less for health care.

"People living in poverty don't have discretionary income," is the typical response I get when I talk about being willing to pay the full costs of good food. "They can't afford either good food or health care." Admittedly, for people living in poverty, choosing good food is more of a challenge. Some poor people may spend up to half of their income for food. For these people, spending another ten to twenty percent for food would require five to ten percent more income since they can't take it from anywhere else in their budget. But, the challenge can be met.

First, from each dime the average American consumer spends for food, about eight cents goes to pay for the processing, transportation, storage, and packaging that makes food more convenient, and for the advertising that persuades people that convenience is more important than food. So the average consumer actually spends only about two cents from each dollar of their income for food — for what they actually eat. This means lower income consumers spending half of their income for food are being persuaded to spend about forty percent of their income for convenience, rather than food.

Lower income consumers often buy food in smaller quantities, buy more highly processed foods, and buy more pre-prepared, take-out, or fast foods. Many don't have the money to buy in bulk, don't have freezers for food storage, and don't have time to prepare food because they are working long hours or two jobs. As a result, the poor may actually spend proportionally more for convenience and less for food than does the average consumer.

Obviously, a poor person can't afford to buy as much of *everything* as a wealthy person can. So, poor people may not be able to afford both *good food* and the level of *convenience* that many Americans have come to expect with their food. But they can choose between good food and convenience, even if they can't afford both. If a person spending fifty percent of their income on food was able to buy all of their food from local producers in its raw or unprocessed form, they could theoretically save the equivalent of forty percent of their income simply by buying food locally and preparing their own food. They would avoid the eighty percent of total food costs accounted for by processing, transportation, storage, packaging, and advertising.

Realistically, no one can actually save this entire amount, as it would require slaughtering animals for meat, milling grain for bread, and so on.

In addition, some raw food items, such as raw milk, are not sold direct from farmers to consumers in many locations. But it is realistic to believe that most consumers could save half or more of the cost they currently pay for convenience by buying locally and preparing their own food. Practically all vegetables and many fruits and berries are readily available to consumers from local farmers during their normal local growing seasons. Meat, milk, and eggs are often available locally in minimally processed forms. Flour for bread and grains for cereal are often available directly, if not locally, from a miller. Some retail food stores also offer raw and minimally processed items bought from local growers.

Every individual situation will be a bit different, but realistically, a person spending half of their income for food might save the equivalent of a twenty to thirty percent of their income by preparing their own food from raw or minimally processed local food items. Hours spent preparing meals can be as economically beneficial as hours spent working for pay. Costs of transportation, childcare, or special clothing may dramatically reduce the *net* income from additional work. A person working long hours, or even two jobs, may actually be better off financially after cutting back to a normal workweek and preparing their own food. Thus, the economic obstacles to good eating are surmountable.

The obstacles of being unable to buy in bulk, unable to store food, and lack of time also can be overcome, with a bit of education and some common sense. The costs of additional equipment for food preparation or transportation for local shopping will probably be more than offset by avoiding the expenses of a second job. Buying food in larger quantities when the weekly paycheck comes in is as easy as setting aside a few dollars for savings. Bulk buying actually is an investment that will be paid back with interest with each meal prepared. The money saved on food during times when many local foods are in-season can quickly pay off an investment in canning equipment or a second-hand freezer. Anyone with normal intelligence and an able body can afford to eat good food.

To demonstrate the practicality of eating good local food on a "food stamp budget," Robert Waldrop, president of the Oklahoma Food Alliance, tried it for a week. He combined (1) frugal supermarket shopping, (2) preparing meals from basic ingredients, (3) buying local foods, (4) gardening, (5) food storage, and (6) home preservation of food to create a healthy, affordable, practical, and environmentally sustainable meal plan. And, he said, "the food had to be satisfying and taste good too, otherwise, what's the point?"

The bottom line, he was able to provide a healthy diet for two people with seventy-three percent local foods for a cost of just over $60, a bit less than the current food stamp allowance for two people. Waldrop's website (www.bettertimesinfo.org/foodchallenge.htm) provides many more details. His basic point, even poor people can afford good local food.

A commitment to eating good food represents far more than a change in shopping habits. It is a commitment to a new lifestyle for everyone who makes it, but is even more so for people with low incomes. First, a person with less income is not likely to have the nutrition education necessary to choose a low-cost, healthy diet from the smaller seasonal variety of locally available foods. Second, they may also lack the necessary skills for food preparation, processing, and storage. However, most people probably realize they can overcome these deficiencies if they had a good reason to do so. Publicly supported educational programs are available for anyone who is interested in learning to select and prepare their own food. But self-education requires a personal commitment.

The lack of time for food preparation may seem more difficult. However, families that are willing to make a commitment to good food may find they actually have more time for the things that they now find important in life. First, some local foods, such as fresh vegetables, fruits, and cheese, require little preparation. In addition, children of all ages, and both genders, can be productive participants in food preparation and processing. Families can rediscover the true meaning of *quality time* preparing good food and enjoying it together. Time devoted to preparing and eating good food can be time for learning, for creative expression, and for sharing of values and culture among family and friends, not time wasted. Time spent preparing food also leaves less time to be filled with unproductive, counterproductive, and often costly distractions.

Even families with limited income may find that they can actually live better by spending more time and money for good local food and less of both on other things that are no longer *necessities* in a family that shares an appreciation for good food. People, rich and poor, need only find the courage to reject the bombardment of advertising that tells them food is nothing but fuel to be purchased as cheaply as possible, prepared easily as possible, and consumed as quickly as possible. The enjoyment of preparing and eating good, sustainably produced, local food is well worth the extra time, effort, and money.

2005

31 | Top Ten Reasons for Eating Local

Some people seem perfectly happy with foods they find in the supermarkets and franchise restaurants of our increasingly global, industrial food system. But, a lot of us are not. A growing body of statistics is indicating that people increasingly want to *eat local;* they want to buy food from people they know and can trust. Recent surveys have shown:

• Seventy-three percent of Americans want to know whether food is grown or produced locally or regionally.

• Seventy-five percent of consumers, in seven Midwestern states and in Boston and Seattle areas, give top priority to produce "grown locally by family farmers."

• Seventy percent of households, in Nebraska, Iowa, Missouri, and Wisconsin, indicate it is very or extremely important to support local family farms by eating locally grown foods.

• Shoppers who buy "natural" foods overwhelmingly choose freshness as their top priority.

Increasingly, people are acting on their preferences for local eating as evidenced by a doubling of the number of farmers' markets in less than ten years, persistent growth in the number of CSAs, and the growing number of independent restaurants and food stores relying on local foods for their market advantage. Why are more people choosing to eat local? Everyone has his or her personal reason, of course, but I developed my "Top Ten List," primarily for the benefit of those who may feel a bit intimidated by those who consider choosing to eat local a bit strange.

I chose to rank my list from the least important to most important reasons. Others obviously would rank them differently, but my ranking reflects my belief that the roots of change in Americans' food preferences go far deeper than food quality or safety. I believe that buying more food locally could be an important step toward solving some deep-rooted problems of the American food system, and ultimately, of American society.

10. **Eating local eliminates the middlemen.** Transportation, energy, packing, advertising, and middlemen profits account for about 25 percent of total food cost, all of which can be greatly reduced by eating local. However, local farmers generally cannot afford to operate on as small a margin of return to their land, labor, and management as can large-scale, global, industrial operations. In addition, industrial producers externalize some of their production costs by exploiting nature and society. So, local foods may not be cheaper, but eliminating middlemen certainly reduces the negative social and ecological consequences of our food choices.

9. **Eating local saves transportation costs.** Recent estimates indicate that the average fresh-food item travels 1,500 miles from production to final purchase. Transportation costs amounts to only about four percent of food costs, but this doesn't count the cost of publicly funded infrastructure. In addition, energy for transportation is virtually all derived from non-renewable fossil fuels and transportation is a major source of air pollution. By eating local, we can make a significant contribution to social and ecological sustainability through our personal statement in favor of reducing our dependence on non-renewable energy and protecting the natural environment.

8. **Eating local improves food quality.** Local foods can be fresher, more flavorful, and nutritious than can fresh foods shipped in from distant locations. According to most surveys, this reason would top most lists of those who choose to eat locally. In addition to the obvious advantage in freshness, growers who produce for local customers need not give priority to harvesting, packing, shipping, and shelf-life qualities, but instead can select, grow, and harvest crops to ensure peak qualities of freshness, nutrition, and taste. Eating local also encourages eating seasonally, in harmony with the natural energy of a particular place, which is becoming an important dimension of quality for many of us.

7. **Eating local makes at-home eating worth the time and effort.** Preparing local foods, which typically are raw or minimally processed, requires additional time and effort. But the superior quality of local foods allows almost anyone to prepare really good foods at home. Good local

foods taste good naturally, with little added seasoning and little cooking or slow cooking, which requires little attention. Home preparation of raw foods also saves money, compared with convenience foods, which makes good food affordable for almost anyone who can and will prepare food from scratch, regardless of income. Preparing and eating meals at home also provides opportunities for families to share quality time together in creative, productive, and rewarding activities, which contribute to stronger families, communities, and societies.

6. **Eating local provides more meaningful food choices.** Americans often brag about the incredible range of choices that consumers have in the modern supermarket today. In many respects, however, food choices are severely limited. Virtually all of food items in supermarkets today are produced using the same mass-production, industrial methods, with the same negative social and ecological consequences. In addition, the variety in foods today is largely cosmetic and superficial, contrived to create the illusion of diversity and choice where none actually exists. By eating local, food buyers can get the food they individually prefer by choosing from foods that are authentically different, not just in physical qualities but also in terms of the ecological and social consequences of how they are produced.

5. **Eating local contributes to the local economy.** American farmers, on average, receive only about 20 cents of each dollar spent for food, the rest going for processing, transportation, packing, and other marketing costs. Farmers who sell food direct to local customers, however, receive the full retail value, a dollar for each food dollar spent. Of course, each dollar not spent at a local supermarket or eating establishment, detracts something from the local economy. But the local *food* economy still gains about three dollars for each dollar lost when food shoppers choose to buy from local farmers. In addition, farmers who produce for local markets receive a larger proportion of the total as a return for their labor, management, and entrepreneurship because they contribute a larger proportion to the production process. They also tend to spend locally, both for their personal and farming needs, which contribute still more to the local economy. Eating local is good for the local economy.

4. **Eating local helps save farmland.** More than one million acres of U.S. farmland is lost each year to residential and commercial development. We are still as dependent upon the land for our very survival today as when all people were hunters and gatherers, and future generations will be no less dependent than we are today. Our dependencies are more complex and

less direct, but certainly are no less critical. Eating local creates economic opportunities for caring farmers to care for and retain control of their land while valuing their neighbors as customers. Farms that don't impose environmental and social costs on their neighbors can be very desirable places to live on and to live around. Eating local may allow new residential communities to be established *on* farms, with residences strategically placed to retain the best land in farming. New sustainable communities could be built around common interests in good food and good lifestyles.

3. **Eating local allows people to reconnect.** The industrial food system was built upon a foundation of impersonal, economic relationships among farmers, food processors, food distributors, and consumers. Relationships had to be made impartial and impersonal to gain economic efficiency. As a result, however, many people today have no meaningful understanding of where their food comes from or how it is produced. By eating local, people are able to reconnect with local farmers, and through local farmers, reconnect with the earth. Many people first begin to understand a need to reconnect when they develop personal relationships with their farmers and personal knowledge of their farms. We cannot build a sustainable food system until people develop a deep understanding of their dependency upon each other and upon the earth. Thus, in my opinion, reconnecting is one of the most important reasons for eating local.

2. **Eating local restores integrity to the food system.** A sustainable food system must be built upon a foundation of personal integrity. When people eat locally, farmers form relationships with customers who care about the social and ecological consequences of how their food is produced — not just lower price or more convenience. Those who eat locally form relationships with farmers who care about their land, their neighbors, and their customers — not just about maximizing profits. Such relationships become relationships of trust and integrity, based on honesty, fairness, compassion, responsibility, and respect. Eating local provides people with an opportunity not only to reconnect personally, but also, to restore integrity to our relationships with each other and with the earth. In today's society, there can be fewer if any higher priorities.

1. **Eating local helps build a sustainable society.** The growing problems that confront today's food system are but reflections of deeper problems within the whole of American society. We are degrading the ecological integrity of the earth and the social integrity of our society in our pursuit of narrow, individual economic self-interests. Some may argue that Americans will never agree on the principles that define the integrity of

our relationships. However, such arguments mistake values for principles. I believe virtually all Americans agree that people should be honest, fair, responsible, compassionate, and respectful. Who among us really believes it to be right and good to be dishonest, unfair, irresponsible, unkind, and disrespectful? Relationships of integrity are essential for sustainability, not just for our food system but also for the whole of our society and the future of humanity. There can be no higher reason for eating local than helping to restore integrity to our society.

2005

32 | Americans: Overfed & Undernourished

*A*mericans are the most obese people in the world. According to the Center for Disease Control and Prevention, adult obesity has increased by 60% within the past twenty years. Trends for childhood obesity are even worse, having *doubled* for children and *tripled* for adolescents during the same time. One-third of American adults are now considered severely overweight or obese. Obesity is closely linked with other health problems, particularly diabetes and heart disease, and ranks second only to tobacco smoking as a cause of adult death. Americans are the most overfed yet undernourished people in the world.

The epidemic of obesity is obviously related to the American diet. It might be easy to blame these maladies on the sedentary but high-stress American lifestyle, which probably is a significant causal factor. But an even more important cause might be the lack of essential nutrients in many of today's foods. A growing number of scientific studies are finding significant declines in the nutritional value of our foods. And dramatic drops in nutrient density have occurred during a period when American farms were under pressure to specialize, mechanize, and get bigger — to produce more food cheaper.

Farm policy has always been promoted to taxpayers as being necessary to provide food security. The USDA defines food security as "access by all people at all times to enough food for an active, healthy life." Food security, however, includes food *quality* as well as *quantity* and affordability. If food isn't nutritious and healthful, as well as available and affordable, it will not ensure adequate diets for all. Unfortunately, the emphasis of food security programs administered through the USDA — including its farm programs — has been on food quantity rather than food quality. The agency admits its concept of food security is not adequate to ensure healthy diets, but places most of the burden for food quality on consumers.

During the 1930s, USDA farm programs were justified as means of keeping farmland in the trusted care of family farmers who had very personal reasons for maintaining the fertile and productive quality of their land. At the time, farmers produced much of their own food and most non-farm consumers were their neighbors. As the population became more urban, price and farm income support programs were promoted as a means of stabilizing prices to ensure a dependable and affordable food supply for all. More recently, the emphasis of agricultural policy has shifted from domestic food production to reliance on the global food economy. The emphasis is on enhancing agricultural exports, but the underlying assumption is that international trade will make food more abundant and affordable for Americans.

Meanwhile the evidence continues to grow that cheap food is abundant in calories but deficient in nutrients. For example, problems of obesity and diabetes are more common among people with lower incomes who logically tend to seek foods providing the cheapest source of energy — meaning the most calories for the fewest dollars. Because of time constraints, many such people also rely heavily on highly processed and ready-to-eat foods, including "fast foods." On such diets, people can easily end up eating far more calories than they need without getting enough nutrition to meet the minimum requirements of a healthy diet.

When livestock are offered a wide variety of foodstuffs containing a variety of vitamins, minerals, and other nutrients, most will naturally select a healthy balanced diet. When offered a premixed feed containing fixed quantities of the same nutrients, they tend to consume more of some nutrients than they need, apparently trying to meet their minimum requirements of others. If we humans have this same basic tendency, whenever our food choices are limited we will tend to consume more of some nutrients than we need because we are not getting enough of others. In other words, a lack of nutrient balance in our diets would leave us hungry, even though we are consuming far more calories than is consistent with good health. Many Americans may be obese, sedentary, and stressed-out because they are starving for nutritional substance in their foods.

One prominent academic study compared nutrient levels in 43 garden crops in 1999 with levels documented in benchmark nutrient studies conducted by USDA in 1950. The scientists found declines in median concentrations of six important nutrients: protein – 6%, calcium – 16%, phosphorus – 9%, iron – 15%, riboflavin – 38%, and vitamin C – 2%. While these essential nutrients may be lacking in most foods today, they may be found in abundance in foods grown naturally and organically on healthy, productive soils. (For studies of health benefits of natural foods, see *The Organic Center,* www.organic-center.org.) A 1993 study comparing conventional foods with organic foods found that organically grown apples, potatoes, pears, wheat, and sweet corn, purchased over a two-year period, averaged 63% higher in calcium, 73% higher in iron, 118% higher in magnesium, 91% higher in phosphorus, 125% higher in potassium, and 60% higher in zinc than conventional foods purchased at the same times.

Other studies establish clear links between declining nutrient density and the industrialization of American agriculture. One such study found that yield-enhancing technologies — fertilizers, pesticides, plant density, and irrigation — reduce the nutrient content of field crops by amounts generally consistent with declines in nutrient density over the past 50 years and nutrient differences between conventional and organic crops. These results should come as no surprise to anyone who understands that industrial agriculture profits primarily from *quantity* factors: acres farmed, head produced, yields per acre, rates of gain, and the cost efficiency of large-scale production. Quality factors affecting prices typically are incidental to profits and often related to cosmetic appearance rather than nutrition.

It seems only logical that an industrial agriculture would tend toward selection of crop varieties, livestock breeds, and production systems that rely on organisms having fewer and larger cells that are mostly filled with water. Organisms with smaller cells tend to be more nutrient dense because they contain more cell walls that are formed from the wide variety of nutrients extracted from the soil or air. In addition, conventional crop production relies heavily on the three basic elements of nitrogen, phosphorus, and potash common in most commercial fertilizers. While these elements are obviously adequate to support high-crop yields, they may not be adequate to produce crops containing the wide diversity and balance of nutrients found in crops produced on healthy, naturally productive, organic soils. Even after adjusting for moisture content, less nutrient-dense foods appear to be cheaper and more profitable to produce. Regardless, this line of inquiry would appear to be a potentially fertile ground for continuing research into questions of food quality and nutrition. But we don't need a mountain of evidence to conclude that food quality has been compromised in the pursuit of agricultural productivity.

The food processing and distribution industry also must share the blame. The corporations that market our foods are concerned about profits — not diet or health. In fact, the managers of the multinational corporations that currently control the American food system have a legal fiduciary responsibility to maximize returns to their stockholders. They have no social or ethical commitment to protecting public health and instead do only those things required by law. Current laws are clearly inadequate to protect the public from diet related illnesses, as is evident in current trends in the diets and health of Americans.

Food industry marketers know that humans have a natural taste preference, probably a genetic predisposition, for foods that are high in fat and sugar. Preferences essential for the survival and health of our primitive ancestors may threaten our health today. Regardless, it's easier to market foods that are higher in calories, particularly when those foods are cheaper to produce. The primary sources of those cheap calories are plants and animals from farms using modern yield-enhancing technologies and thus lacking in nutrient density and encouraging over consumption while enhancing food industry profits. Some logical health consequences of such diets are obesity, diabetes, and heart disease.

The natural link between agricultural policy, overproduction of nutrient deficient food, and unhealthy diets is skillfully documented in Michael Pollan's best-selling book, *The Omnivore's Dilemma.* He logically links large government subsidies for corn production with surplus production and depressed corn prices, which subsidize manufacturing of the cheap corn sweeteners that now fill the American diet with empty calories in foods ranging from soft drinks to breakfast cereals, to French fries. Corn subsidies also subsidize large-scale confinement feeding of livestock, resulting in too much unhealthy fat in American diets, in addition to a host of other environmental and social problems. A similar story could be told for virtually every food crop subsidized by government programs in the quest for more and cheaper food. It should be obvious that trade policies currently increasing our reliance on cheap industrial foods from other countries will only exacerbate past problems. In attempting to improve food security through government programs designed to make food more abundant and affordable, we have threatened food security by making it less safe and nutritious.

As in the 1930s, the real food security of our nation still depends on keeping farmland in the trusted care of family farmers who are committed to maintaining the fertility and productivity of the land while producing safe and nutritious foods for all. Rather than subsidizing the industrialization of agriculture and promoting cheap food, our farm policies should be refocused on sustaining our smaller, independent family farmers, people who are personally committed to producing good food for their families, their neighbors, and providing food security for their nation. Our food may cost a bit more and we may consume a bit less, but only then, will Americans be well nourished and well fed.

2007

FOOD SECURITY

33 | Small Family Farms for Food Security

ince September 11, 2001, many Americans no longer feel secure. Most concerns seem to focus on physical security — how can we protect ourselves from future terrorist attacks? Others are concerned about economic security — how can we keep terrorism from disrupting the economy? Some are concerned about *short-run* food security — potential threats of bioterrorism to food safety and to the agricultural economy. Perhaps the greatest security risk Americans face, however, is a growing threat to our *long-run* food security — the risk that Americans will not be able to feed themselves, either in times of crisis or tranquility. With our nation seemingly committed both to a single global economy and to a decades-long "war on terrorism," America's food security is at risk.

Americans are losing control over American agriculture. Increasingly, the decisions concerning what will be produced, how much will be produced, where it will be produced, how it will be produced, and who will produce it are being made, not by American citizens, but by multinational corporations. The people who own the land and do the work may still be Americans, but the decisions are being made by someone else, somewhere else. For the most part, contractual arrangements determine who makes the decisions, leaving "producers" as little more than landlords, tractor drivers, or building superintendents, but certainly not in the traditional role of "farmer."

The agribusiness corporations dictating the terms of these contracts are legal entities, but they are not people. They have no families, no friends, no communities, and increasingly, no national citizenship. The people who work for these corporations are real people and are citizens of some nation — with families, friends, and communities. However, people within corporations have no choice other than to serve the economic needs of the corporation for profits and growth, once corporate ownership is separated from management, as in the case of most publicly held corporations. Most investors who have their savings in mutual funds and pension funds, for example, don't even know how many shares of which companies they own. The only reason most such people invest in corporate stock is to increase the value of their savings — to make money. The multinational agribusiness corporations who increasingly control American agriculture have stockholders scattered throughout the world, and thus have no allegiance to any particular nation.

Increasingly, the multinational corporations will find it more profitable to produce somewhere other than in America. Our land and labor costs are simply too high for America to compete with places such as South America, Australia, South Africa, or China in production of basic agricultural commodities, such as corn, soybeans, hogs, cattle, cotton, and rice. We have higher-paying employment opportunities for our labor and higher-valued residential uses for our land. Having no commitment to producing in America, the agribusiness corporations eventually will simply move their operations elsewhere — anywhere that will give their stockholder a higher return on their investment.

In their struggle to stay competitive in global markets, American producers will feel compelled to accept contractual arrangements that result in the exploitation of both land and people. The industrialization of poultry and hog production with large-scale confinement animal feeding operations provides a prime example of such exploitation. These operations consistently pollute the rural environment with odors and waste, yield minimum returns at best for laborers and investors, and drive family farming operations out of business. Even so, they are becoming the only means by which producers can gain access to markets. The same basic trend is already well underway in dairy; and with genetic patenting and biotechnology, corporate control of crop production will soon follow.

Before corporate agriculture abandons America, however, they will have turned much of rural America into a "third-world" wasteland. Polluted streams and groundwater, abandoned waste lagoons, eroded and depleted topsoil, depleted aquifers, rural crime, a de-skilled workforce, and decaying rural communities. These will be the legacies of the corporatization of American agriculture. The people of rural communities will fight back with more environmental rules and regulations, which only increase the incentive for the corporations to locate their production facilities elsewhere in the world, where people are too economically desperate or politically powerless to protect their natural environment. Unfortunately, by then the damage to rural America will have been done. And with a global, "free market" economy, there will be nothing to keep Americans from becoming dependent on food imports.

Economists argue we need not be concerned about depending on imports from other countries for our food. We will be even better fed at a lower cost, they say. But in times of crisis, a nation that can't feed itself is no more secure than is a nation that can't defend itself. Perhaps we won't abandon agriculture completely, but we could easily become as dependent on the rest of the world for our food as we are today for our oil. Perhaps, we can keep our food imports flowing, as we do for oil, but how large a military force will it take, how many small wars will we have to fight, and how many people will be killed.

The food security of America ultimately depends on America's small farms. To sustain the productivity of the land, we must have people on the land who know the land and know how to take care of that land, and who are committed to caring for the land. We must have people on the land who love the land. Today's large-scale, corporate farmers have no particular commitment to any particular piece of land — they don't even own most of the land they farm. They can't really "know their land" because they are trying to farm too much of it to "know any of it" very well. Many don't know how to take care of the land — they depend on commercial inputs for productivity, not on a healthy soil. They can't love the land because their first love must be money if they are going to stay competitive. American food security depends on smaller farms — on having more rather than fewer farms and farmers. Each farmer can only truly love so much land.

To sustain the productivity of the land, people who love the land also must have the time to take care of the land and must be able to afford to take care of the land. This means that we must find ways to make ecologically sound and socially responsible small farms economically viable. We must support a transition from an industrial agriculture to a sustainable agriculture if our food is to be secure. We can encourage a transition from large, industrial farms to smaller sustainable farms by redirecting farm policy toward issues of long run security, making it possible for family farmers to make a decent living on smaller farms. It's absurd to argue that current farm policies ensure food security while those policies subsidize the systems of industrial production and corporate control that are placing our food security at risk. We at least need to quit subsidizing the corporatization of agriculture.

Ultimately, however, Americans must place greater importance on food security than on having food that is simply quick, convenient, and cheap. We must be willing to support a secure, sustainable food system, both with our votes and with our dollars. We can begin by buying as much of our food as we can from local farmers who are committed to sustainability. We can shop at farmers' markets, join CSAs; we can buy at local food stores and restaurants that buy from local growers, and we can participate in public issues that affect the success of smaller, local family farmers.

Can we depend on these small farmers for our future security? We can if we make it possible and profitable for them to stay on the land. Families on small independently owned and operated farms are real people — not some artificial economic entity. They have families, friends, neighbors, and citizenship. Most of them have cultural roots in the land they farm and social roots in the communities where they live. They are not going to quit farming or move their operations to another country just to make a few more dollars in profit or higher returns on their investments. The vast majority of America's small farmers are Americans. They love this land and they love this country. America's food security depends upon the success and sustainability of its smaller family farms.

2001

34 | The High Cost of Cheap Food

*A*t a recent organic farming conference in Winnipeg, Canada, a woman in the audience stood up and said, "Organic foods are not going to become popular with mainstream consumers until they became *quick, convenient, and cheap.*" My immediate response was that *true* organic foods were not going to be quick, convenient, or cheap — at least not for some time to come. Fortunately, more and more people are finding organic foods to be worth the time, effort, and money. Her comment, however, has caused me to think further about the nature of our food system and about what we have done to try to make foods quick, convenient, and cheap for consumers.

First at the farm level, our never-ending quest for cheap food is the root cause of the transformation of American agriculture from a system of small, diversified, independently operated, family farms into a system of large-scale, industrialized, corporately controlled agribusinesses. The production technologies that supported specialization, mechanization, and ultimately, large-scale contract production were all developed to make agriculture more efficient — to make food cheaper for consumers. Millions of American farmers have been forced off the land, the survivors are sacrificing their independence, and thousands of small farming communities have withered and died, all for the sake of cheap food.

These were the consequences of progress, so we were told. The agricultural establishment has boasted loudly that ever-fewer farmers have been able to feed a growing nation with an ever-decreasing share of consumer income spent for food. The increases in economic efficiency have been impressive, but what about the human costs. Economists have totaled up tremendous savings for consumers from lower food costs, but they have never bothered to place a value on the lives of farm families that have been destroyed by the loss of their farms, their way of life, and their heritage. They have never bothered to consider the value of the lives of rural people — with roots in rural schools, churches, and businesses — who were forced to abandon their communities as farm families were forced off the land. The human costs of cheap food have been undeniably tremendous, but since they couldn't be measured in dollars and cents, they have gone uncounted.

The ecological costs of cheap food, likewise not measurable in dollars and cents, also have gone uncounted, and thus, largely ignored. Today, only the most diehard industrialists bother to deny that we have degraded the productivity of the land through erosion and contamination, and that we have polluted the natural environment with agricultural chemicals — in our never-ending pursuit of cheaper food. Certainly, we had soil erosion in the "dust bowl" days, but we were making great strides in soil conservation before the dawning of industrial agriculture in the late 1940s. In spite of stepped up soil conservation efforts of the 1990s, American farms still are losing topsoil at rates far exceeding rates of soil regeneration. Feeble efforts to control soil loss through reduced tillage leave farmers increasingly reliant on herbicides that pollute our streams and groundwater and that disrupt or destroy the biological life in the soil.

All life on earth is rooted in the soil. As farmers destroy the natural productivity of the land, they are destroying the ability of the earth to support life. We are destroying the future of humanity to make agriculture more efficient. What is the value of the future of humanity? Are we in fact willing to risk the future of human life on earth just so we can have cheap food?

With increasing corporate control of agriculture, we may be approaching an end of agriculture in America — at least agriculture as we know it. The globalization of agriculture, through "free-trade" agreements, means that food in the future will be grown wherever in the world it can be produced at the lowest economic cost. High costs of farmland and labor in the United States — consequences of favorable employment opportunities and the urban-to-exurban population migration — may keep U.S. production costs well above costs in other food producing regions of the world. The multinational food corporations that increasingly control agriculture are not people — they have no heart, no soul, nor citizenship in any particular country. They will produce or buy agricultural commodities wherever they can produce or buy at the lowest cost, without regard for national origin. Our continuing quest for cheap food could mean the end of American agriculture.

The United States in the future could well become as dependent on the rest of the world for food as we are today for oil. Economists argue that it doesn't matter where our food is produced; if producing food elsewhere in the world will be cheaper, we will all be better off without agriculture in the United States. But how long will it be before an OFEC (Organization of Food Exporting Countries) is formed to restrict world food supplies causing our food prices to skyrocket, just as we have seen skyrocketing prices of gasoline. Perhaps we can keep food imports flowing through our military might, if economic coercion fails. But, what will be the real costs? How many *small wars* will we have to fight, and how many people will we be "forced to kill" — just for the sake of cheap food? Can we afford the real costs of cheap food?

The costs of making food *quick and convenient* probably are no less than the cost of making food *cheap.* Nearly eighty cents of each dollar Americans spend for food goes to pay for marketing services, such as processing, packaging, transportation, storage, and advertising. All of these costs are associated with making our food convenient — getting it into the most convenient form and package, getting it to the most convenient location, at the most convenient time, and convincing us to buy it. So, we pay far more for the convenience of our food than we pay for the food itself. In fact, we pay more to those who package and advertise our food than we pay to the farmers who produce it. So, by far the greatest part of the total cost of food is the cost of convenience.

Our addiction to convenience also is placing control of our food supply in the hands of a few giant, multinational corporations. As Dr. Bill Heffernan of the University of Missouri has pointed out previously in *Small Farm Today,* the global food supply today is dominated by a handful of giant agribusiness firms, allied by various means, forming three "global food clusters." These firms influence, and in many cases control, nearly everything that happens to our food because they control the processes that make our food "convenient." The price of convenient food is not just the eighty cents of each dollar we spend for food. The greatest cost of convenient food has been the loss of control of our food supply.

The costs of *quick* food are similar in nature to the costs of convenience food. Our growing addiction of "fast food" is evident in the ever-increasing share of our food dollar spent at restaurants and other eating establishments — a share approaching half of total food purchases. And "fast foods" places, such as McDonald's, Kentucky Fried Chicken, Taco Bell, and Pizza Hut account for nearly half of all food consumed away from home. Erick Schlosser, in his recent best seller, *Fast Food Nation*, addresses the cost of our "love affair" with fast foods. He writes, "fast food has triggered the homogenization of our society. Fast food has hastened the malling of our landscape, widening of the chasm between rich and poor, fueled an epidemic of obesity, and propelled the juggernaut of American cultural imperialism abroad." He documents how *quick* food has lured us into choosing diets deficient in nearly everything except calories, supporting practices deceptive in every aspect from advertising to flavoring, and systems that degrade nearly everyone and everything involved in the process.

The fast food industry has lured low-income consumers, along with the affluent, into paying ridiculously high prices for low-quality meats, potatoes, vegetable oil, and sugar. However, the high dollar and cent costs are but the tip of the iceberg. The true costs of quick food must include the costs of poor health, lost dignity in work, degraded landscapes, and ethical and moral decay in business matters, including international trade and investment. We are paying a tremendously high price for the time saved by choosing quick food.

Thankfully, we still have alternatives, at least for many of the things we eat. We can buy from local farmers who are committed to producing foods by ecologically sound and socially responsible means — sustainable farming. We can locate such farmers through "community food circles," which provide directories of local producers who sell direct to consumers. We can shop at farmers' markets, join CSAs, and eat at restaurants that buy from local farmers or seek out items in the independent food stores that are supplied by local sustainable growers.

The food we buy from these local people may not be as quick, convenient, or cheap as the food we could buy at a local fast food joint or supermarket. But it may well be more than worth the time, effort, and money that we have to spend to get it. A friend of mine is fond of saying, "eating is a moral act." It is. The food we choose has an impact upon the lives of other people, upon the earth, and upon the future of humanity. When all of the costs are counted, we simply cannot afford the high costs of cheap food.

2001

35 | Who's Paying for Your Food?

ecently, I was asked by an editor of an organic food magazine to respond to a reader's question asking why organic foods in the supermarkets always seem to cost more than other foods. I answered with the following:

"Most organic foods cost more than most conventional foods today for several reasons. The most fundamental reason is that the dollar and cent cost of conventional foods do not reflect their "full cost" of production. Producers of conventional foods don't pay the ecological costs associated with their degradation of the natural environment. They don't pay for the social costs of the demise of family farms, the decay of rural communities, and the loss of a rural culture of stewardship. And, they don't pay the costs of the growing risk to human health — including pesticide and hormone residues in foods, antibiotic resistant bacteria, and a national epidemic of obesity. Organic farmers' costs of production are higher because they farm in ways that do not create the ecological and social costs associated with conventional, industrial production methods. And, organic farmers don't put the public health at risk in order to minimize their production costs.

That said, many organic products can be produced by many organic farmers at costs equal to or lower than conventional products produced by most conventional farmers. But this level of productivity generally results after years of experience for a highly skilled farmer working with the same piece of land. Marketing and distribution costs also tend to be higher for organic foods simply because the marketing system is less well developed. Over time, as more organic farmers gain more experience, as more research is devoted to organic production methods, and as organic markets become more efficient, we can expect the dollar and cent costs of organic foods to fall. Over time, we also can expect the costs of food provided by the corporately controlled industrial conventional food system to rise.

In time, organic foods may actually cost less than industrial foods. In the meantime, however, consumers will simply have to decide for themselves whether they are willing to pay the full cost of their food, or instead, are willing to impose the ecological and social costs of their food upon someone else."

I make no claim of originality for my answer; the reasons organic foods typically costs more are well known. But never before had it become so clear to me as when drafting this response, that someone is actually paying the full costs of our food even if we are not. We tend to think of cheap food as a wise choice — we are getting more for less, so we think. But, we should be willing to look beyond price and ask *why* some food is cheap and other food is expensive. We need to ask who's paying the full cost of our food.

Some reasons why *local* organic food costs more have been provided by a couple of my University of Missouri friends, Mary Hendrickson and Jose Garcia. In her recent food column in the *Columbia Daily Tribune*, Melinda Hemmelgarn quotes Mary:

"Locally produced food or organic food represents more nearly the true cost of food production. There are many subsidies associated with the way we grow the bulk of our food in the United States. For example, much of the food that grocery stores feature comes from California, Texas and Florida, and even Mexico and Latin America. In California, growers receive water that is federally subsidized to help offset costs. We also have an incredible system of roads and cheap fuel that are taxpayer subsidized.

In many parts of the U.S., produce is picked with migrant labor farm workers who do not receive adequate wages for maintaining even a minimal quality of life. Housing is substandard, and there are few health insurance programs. Schooling for children is a problem, and migrant farm workers face debilitating injuries from the repetitive work and sometimes from the chemicals that are applied to commercial-scale vegetables."

Jose continued the theme of unpaid costs of migrant workers in his response to Melinda's column by asking:

"Would you be willing to have back-breaking, repetitive work with no health insurance, unacceptable housing, and very little money? Migrant workers do, and that helps some of your food coming from California or Florida to be 'cheap.' Health issues for farm workers are only one of the many issues they face such as labor, wages, legal, education, and housing."

So who has paid the costs of food that we haven't paid? Some have been paid by family farmers who have been driven to the verge of bankruptcy by exploitative competition. Some have been paid by rural communities that have withered and died as farm families have been forced off the land by low commodity prices. And some have been paid by migrants and other farm workers who could see no alternative to exploitative wages and working conditions. These unpaid costs are paid by people who, through no fault of their own, have found themselves at the mercy of others who have more economic power.

Other food costs that don't show up in food prices are paid in the form of taxes. In recent years, taxpayers have paid an average of $15 billion per year to subsidize production of corn, soybeans, wheat, rice, sugar, and other basic farm commodities. And as Mary pointed out, some of the taxes that go to subsidize water in the West, to building and repairing interstate highways, and to the military costs of keeping fuel costs low are actually unpaid costs of "cheap food." So what does it matter if we pay the government or the grocery store, as long as we pay one way or the other? The problem is that most of the tax benefits go to those who are exploiting the people who produce food and the land it is produced on, not to reward those who produce food responsibly.

For the most part, government subsidies go to the large, specialized industrial agricultural producers at the expense of small, independent farmers who try to support their communities and try to care for the land. These large, commercial operations typically rely heavily on hired labor, agricultural chemicals, mechanization, and distant markets, all of which tend to be exploitative of people, non-renewable resources, and the land. The ecologically and socially responsible family farmers who receive government payments typically get barely enough to put in another crop.

Much, if not most, of our unpaid food costs are being billed to our children, grandchildren, and others of future generations. When our choice of "cheap food" leads to environmental degradation and social injustice, we are not really avoiding those costs; we are simply charging them to future generations. Those of future generations can't express their preferences and values either in the marketplace or at the ballot box. They can't choose to pay the full cost of food nor can they redirect government programs. They must depend on us to ensure that they will have land capable of producing enough food and a society capable of ensuring equity and opportunity. Our failure to pay the full cost of food today is destroying the productivity of our land and the civility of our society. Much of the unpaid cost of our food is simply being put on a charge account to be paid off by our children's children and their children.

Of course, paying high prices is no guarantee that food is produced by ecologically and socially responsible means. Some of the highest priced foods, particularly highly processed food and food eaten in restaurants, are produced under the some of the most oppressive working conditions and come from the most highly industrialized production operations. Neither is buying high-priced organic food a sure means of paying the full costs of food. Increasingly, organic foods in supermarkets are produced by large industrial, migrant labor operations in California, Florida, and Mexico. Actually, "fair priced" food need not be expensive, particularly if we are willing to take the time and make the effort to process and prepare it for ourselves, and even those with little income can afford to pay the full cost of good food.

The best way to pay a fair price for food is to know as much as we can about how our food was produced, where it was produced, and who produced it. Then we should ask, what are the ecological and social implications of our food choices? The easiest way to answer these questions is to buy locally, from someone we know, at farmers markets, through CSAs — directly from farmers we know and trust. But, we are not necessarily limited to direct, local food sources. We can buy from food retail operators and restaurateurs that we trust to buy locally or to buy only from producers and suppliers they know they can trust.

Of course, most of us don't have realistic opportunities to buy every-thing we eat from someone we know well enough to know if they are responsible producers. But the more we look, the more sources we will find, and the more opportunities we will create for producers who have the courage to ask their customers to pay the full cost of food. Someday, hopefully, we will all have an opportunity to pay and will be willing to pay the full cost of food. In the meantime, however, we will each have to decide for ourselves whether we are willing to pay the full cost of our food, or instead, are willing to impose the ecological and social costs of our food upon someone else.

2003

36 Meeting the Challenge of Peak Oil with Sustainable Agriculture

*H*igher prices for gasoline and other fossil fuels have renewed public interest in alternative sources of renewable energy, including wind, water, photovoltaic, and biofuels. High energy prices in 2005 were due in part to unpredictable events, such as hurricane Katrina, but the approaching peak in global oil production makes even higher energy prices both predictable and inevitable. *Peak oil* is a concept based on the premise that peaks in oil production occur when approximately half of the total amount of oil in a particular oil field has been extracted, which typically occurs some 30 to 40 years after the initial discovery. Beyond that point, extraction becomes increasingly difficult and costly, and total production inevitably declines.

Peak oil gained credibility when U.S. domestic oil production peaked in 1970, thirty-plus years following the peak in U.S. oil discoveries in the 1930s. The peak in global oil discoveries occurred later, in the mid-1960s, signaling a peak in global oil production around the turn of the twenty-first century. Changes in extraction methods and uncertainty regarding Middle East oil reserve data have made precise calculations difficult, but most forecasters now place the year of global peak oil somewhere between 2006 and 2010. Even more optimistic government forecasts indicate a peak in global production between 2010 and 2020, with a 70 percent decline in total oil production by 2050. If major new oil fields were discovered next year, which is highly unlikely, those fields would not reach peak production for another 30 to 40 years. The world quite simply must learn to live with less oil.

A transition to biological energy sources is not the solution. The renewable energy produced annually by all types of plant life within the U.S. amounts to only about two-thirds as much as total annual U.S. use of non-renewable fossil energy. Agriculture is able to harvest only a little more than 35 percent of total plant energy produced — an amount equivalent to about 25 percent of total U.S. fossil energy use. Total energy used by U.S. agriculture amounts to an equivalent of about 6 percent of total fossil energy use. This might appear to indicate a significant energy surplus for agriculture. However, crops that could be consumed directly by humans account for only about 20 percent of total agricultural energy production. The remaining 80 percent is produced by pastures and forages, which are utilized by livestock in producing meat, milk, eggs, and other food products. In addition, about 90 percent of all food crops produced in the U.S. is fed to livestock and poultry, which on average require more than 15 kcal of fossil energy for each kcal of food products. As a result, U.S. agriculture actually uses about three kcal of fossil energy for each kcal of food energy produced.

In addition, agriculture accounts for only about one-third of total energy used for U.S. food production, including food processing and distribution, the total being equivalent to about 17 percent of total fossil energy used. The U.S. food system in total requires approximately 10 kcal of fossil energy to produce each kcal of food energy, in addition to the solar energy harvested by agricultural plants. Agriculture alone cannot possibly produce enough biofuels to offset the future decline in fossil fuel production. In fact, agriculture faces a formidable challenge in producing enough renewable energy to meet the growing global food and fiber needs.

Shifting to a vegetarian diet would be one obvious means of reducing energy use in agriculture since most food crops are net energy producers, possibly cutting the food energy input/output ratio in half. However, energy used and lost in food processing and distribution would still leave about a five-to-one net fossil energy deficit for total food production. In addition, the 20 percent fossil fuel equivalent produced by pastures and forage plants — large net energy producers — would be lost. Shifting from confinement livestock feeding operations to grass-based operations could be a more logical means of reducing the energy used in animal agriculture. A shift to grass-based systems could save an estimated 35 percent of total energy now used in beef, dairy, and lamb production.

Other sustainable farming practices could reduce agricultural energy use still farther. For example, research based on more than 20 years of recent data indicates that shifting to organic farming practices could save as much as 30 percent of the fossil energy, without reducing total production. Sustainable grass-based livestock systems, utilizing management intensive grazing, are capable of producing from 50 percent to 100 percent more protein per acre than conventional pasture/forage systems, while using less fertilizer, pesticides, and fuel. Free-range and pasture-based pork and poultry also are far more energy efficient than confinement feeding operations. In addition, hogs and chickens are natural scavengers and thus could get a significant portion of their diets from waste products. Significant fossil energy savings from livestock and poultry might well be achievable without sacrificing healthy levels of animal protein in human diets. Changes in food processing and distribution in the United States, such as increased use of raw and minimally processed foods, more meals prepared at home, and a shift to more community-based, local food systems could increase the efficiency of energy use in food marketing by comparable amounts.

To my knowledge, no detailed estimates are available, but energy savings from shifting to more-sustainable agricultural systems, using currently available methods and technologies, probably could cut total fossil energy use in agriculture by one-half, resulting in a savings equivalent to about 3 percent of total fossil energy use. Similar efficiencies in processing and distribution could save an additional 6 percent or so in fossil energy use, but would still leave total food production with an energy deficit equivalent to 8 percent of current total fossil energy use in the United States.

Despite the current enthusiasm for biological sources of renewable energy, it seems unlikely that agriculture of the future will be able to produce more energy than will be needed to meet the increasing food and fiber needs of people. Current agricultural energy initiatives, specifically those utilizing grain and oilseeds to produce ethanol and biodiesel, have shown little promise of ever generating significantly more energy than they consume. Their primary value seems to be in changing the form of energy, to provide fuel for motor vehicles, rather than increasing the total amount of energy available. With a growing world population, reducing the amount of fossil energy required for food production would seem a far higher public priority than turning potential food for hungry people into fuel for automobiles.

Farms may have far more to contribute in meeting future energy challenges as locations for wind generators than as producers of energy crops. Some current estimates indicate that wind energy could eventually replace up to 60 percent of current fossil energy use. However, achieving this level of production would require large investments in energy transmission infrastructure in addition to thousands of wind turbines. Wind energy advocates are currently promoting the development of huge wind farms populated by dozens to hundreds of multi-million dollar generators. However, such initiatives reflect the industrial-era thinking that created the energy problem, rather than a sustainable energy paradigm for the future. A sustainable energy system must be able to realize the benefits of specialization, standardization, and consolidation of control, but without sacrificing the diversity, site specificity, individuality, and decentralization necessary to maintain the capacity for renewal and regeneration.

On sustainable farms, wind turbines would be integrated into the overall farming operation, utilizing a diversity of sizes and strategic locations to accommodate other farming activities. On large, specialized wind farms, turbines occupy about 2 percent of land area. On sustainable farms, the competition for space between generators and farming would be insignificant. Smaller turbines in less concentrated patterns at many different locations might be less technically efficient but would minimize potential noise pollution and other environmental concerns and would prevent the tremendous concentration of economic and political power that otherwise will be associated with energy generation in the future. Supplemental income from energy generation would also help diversity and sustain large numbers of small- to moderate-sized farming operations. Sustainable energy will require ecological integrity and social responsibility as well as economic efficiency.

A sustainable wind energy system likely would be a decentralized network, linking hundreds of thousands of farms and ranches with various numbers and types of wind generators. Windmills would be scattered across the North American West and Great Plains as well as other specific areas with wind energy potential. The same transmission lines bringing electricity to these farms and ranches could be used to carry wind-generated energy back to the major retransmission points within the network. Such a network would also allow farmers to help close energy cycles on their farms by utilizing plant and animal wastes to generate electricity. However, such a system would require a fundamentally different type of infrastructure and organizational paradigm from that envisioned for giant, specialized wind farms.

In meeting the challenge of peak oil, we must not allow agriculture to be viewed with the same industrial mindset that has made the global economy so completely dependent on fossil fuel. Ultimately, we must embrace a material standard of living that will allow *unavoidable* losses of nonrenewable energy to be offset by energy captured by living plants, windmills, falling water, photovoltaic, and other sources of solar energy. To meet the challenge of peak oil we must respect the rights of those of future generations to meet their energy needs as we find ways to meet ours, not just find another source of cheap nonrenewable energy to last through our lifetime. A sustainable agriculture can help, but meeting the peak oil challenge ultimately will depend on the willingness of human society to embrace the ecological, social, and economic principles of sustainability.

2005

Most energy percentages used are based on data from, David and Marcia Pimentel, ed., 1996, Food, Energy, and Society, *University Press of Colorado, Niwot, CO.*

37 Healthy Farms, Healthy Foods, Healthy Society

I am often impressed with other speakers at venues where I have opportunities to speak. In recent weeks, several speakers have emphasized the links between human health and our natural environment. One was Chip Ward, a concerned resident of Utah, who wrote in his book, *Canaries on the Rim,* "The most direct link you have with your environment is your own body and its health. Your body is composed of more than a trillion cells that are constantly renewed. Every year of your life, you have a new liver, new marrow, new stomach lining, and so on. Breast cells turn over monthly. New cells have to come from somewhere and they come from the foods we eat, the fluids we drink, and the air we breathe. Our environment becomes us as soil, plant, animal, water, and air are processed into our flesh and blood." We become what we eat; it's a self-evident truth.

Another speaker, Carolyn Raffensperger, Director of the Science and Environmental Health Network (SEHN) writes, "The health of Earth's ecosystem is the foundation of all health. Human impact in the form of population pressure, resource abuse, economic self-interest, and inappropriate technologies is rapidly degrading the environment. This impact, in turn, is creating new patterns of human and ecosystem poverty and disease. The tension among ecosystem health, public health, and individual health is reaching a breaking point at the beginning of the twenty-first Century."

In spite of popular claims to the contrary, we are becoming a society of increasingly unhealthy people. The popular claims for greater health typically begin with the statement that we Americans are living longer than before, but such claims conveniently ignore the state of health during those longer years. Illnesses are often the result of a complexity of genetic, social, and environmental interactions, but we cannot ignore dramatic increases in certain types of illnesses that are logically related to the air we breathe, water we drink, and food we eat. Scientific sources for the following statements can be found on the SEHN website www.sehn.org/pppra.html.

• Childhood cancers increased by 10.2 percent between 1973 and 1991, and today, one in every 400 North American children is expected to develop cancer before age 15.

• About 25 percent of all Americans in 1950 would be diagnosed with cancer during their lifetime; by 1997, that figure had risen to 40 percent.

• Testicular cancer has doubled in the past 20 years in the U.S., and over the past 50 years, a 53 percent decline in sperm count has been documented among men in all industrialized countries.

• An American woman's chances of developing breast cancer during her lifetime have gone from 1 in 20 in 1960 to 1 in 8 in 1999, and now, is approaching 1 in 5.

• Type I (insulin dependent) diabetes doubled between 1964 and 1981, and continues to increase each year.

• Asthma in children ages 6 to 11 increased 58 percent from 1971 to 1980 and has been doubling every 20 years over the past several decades.

• At least 3 to 6 percent of children in the U.S. now have documented cases of ADHD (Attention Deficit Hyperactivity Disorder) and the actual rates may in fact be much higher.

While it is difficult to prove, or disprove, direct cause and effect relationships between environmental pollution and diseases, the following consequences of industrial development, including industrial agriculture, have occurred during the periods of increasing health problems in America mentioned above.

• U.S. production of synthetic chemicals increased a hundred-fold from 1920 to the end of the 1980s, mostly after World War II, and now tops five-trillion pounds each year.

• Of the more than 70,000 synthetic chemicals now in use, fewer than 1,600 have been tested for carcinogenicity.

• About 2.23 billion pounds of pesticides are used each year in the U.S.; 82 percent of households use pesticides, 50 percent use weed killers, and

50 percent use flea treatments; and only about 10 percent of pesticides in use have received comprehensive toxicological testing.

• Of the 2.26 billion pounds of toxic chemicals released into the environment in 1994, 177 million pounds of them were known carcinogens.

• Forty possible carcinogens have been found in the water we drink, 60 have been found in the air we breathe, and 66 in the food crops we eat.

• The chemical industry continues to grow at a rate of 3.5 percent per year, doubling in size every 20 years.

Admittedly, there is no conclusive scientific *proof* of direct linkages between most chemicals in our environment and increased incidences of cancer, diabetes, or respiratory problems, just as there was no scientific proof of a link between cigarette smoking and lung cancer in the early 1970s. However, we know that many of the toxic chemicals in our environment are also in our bodies, in breast milk, and in newborn children.

• The average middle-aged U.S. man has detectible residues from 177 different organochlorines, many of which are from known or suspected carcinogens.

• Everyone in the U.S. has detectable levels of DDT and PCBs in their tissues, even though DDT has been banned in this country since 1972.

• By 1976, about 25 percent of human breast milk in the United States was too contaminated with chemicals to have been sold as food, at least some of which were passed on to nursing babies.

• Umbilical cord blood from the newborn child contains PCBs, pesticides, and pthalates.

• Lead, which is not naturally found in the body, is now present in the bodies of humans and all other living things on the planet. About 4.4 million women of childbearing age may have blood lead levels higher than the maximum safe levels for fetuses.

Some may question whether it is necessary, ethical, or even useful to quote this litany of environmental health statistics in the absence of scientific proof of direct causality. I personally believe that people are capable of drawing their own conclusions about such things. In fact, each of us ultimately *must* draw our own conclusions about these issues because they are simply too complex to be resolved using the best of today's scientific methods. Today's science is very good at resolving issues when few significant interactions exist between humans and their environment, and thus, specific causes and effects can be isolated. However, scientists needed more than 20 years to isolate the effects of smoking tobacco on human health, a situation where the number of chemicals was relatively small and the method of delivery was fairly well defined. How long would it take science to untangle the multiple interactions among and reactions of our bodies to the 40 chemicals in the air we breathe, 60 chemicals in the water we drink, and 66 chemicals in the foods we eat? The answer is, too long, even if it is possible.

We know that "our environment becomes *us* as soil, plant, animal, water, and air are processed into our flesh and blood." We shouldn't be breathing, drinking, or eating things that we don't want to become parts of our bodies or the bodies of our children. We don't need to ask permission from scientific experts to refuse to expose our bodies to anything that we think may be detrimental to our health. We don't need to apologize for vigorously resisting involuntary exposure to things that we don't believe to be safe and healthful, regardless of how safe industry scientists may claim them to be. The scientists don't have the answers to complex health issues; we must think for ourselves.

So what does this have to do with sustainable agriculture and small farms? First, "When an activity raises threats of harm to human health or the environment, precautionary measures should be taken even if some cause and effect relationships are not fully established scientifically. In this context the proponent of an activity, rather than the public, should bear the burden of proof. The process of applying the precautionary principle must be open, informed, and democratic and must include potentially affected parties. It must also involve an examination of the full range of alternatives, including no action."

This *precautionary principle* is routinely applied in cases involving human medicine. The drug manufacturer, not the potential patients, must present compelling evidence that a new drug is both safe and effective. The same principle should be followed in environmental health issues, but so far, it's still pretty much up to us as individuals to protect ourselves from environmental risks. So it is up to farmers to protect themselves and their families, as well as their customers and their neighbors, from the environmental health risks of farming. Farmers can choose to practice the precautionary principle even if the government doesn't require it.

The environmental risks associated with agriculture are almost invariably associated with industrial farming methods. The commercial fertilizers, pesticides, and wastes from confinement animal feeding operations, which foul the air, pollute water, and contaminate our foods, are inevitable consequences of industrial agriculture. And as farmers have employed the tools and methods of industrialization, their farms inevitably become larger and even more dependent on technologies such as genetically modified organisms, which now permeate our food supply with inherently uncertain consequences for human health. Large, industrial farms simply are not healthy farms.

Sustainable farming methods, on the other hand, allow farmers to break free of chemical dependency, and in the process, to practice precautionary principles of human health for themselves, their families, their neighbors, and those who eat the foods they produce. Sustainable farming methods allow farmers to sustain their economic viability without growing ever larger and increasingly dependent on the industrial technologies which threaten human health. Healthy farms produce healthy foods, healthy people, healthy communities, healthy economies, and healthy societies.

2006

BIG IDEAS

38 Farming as a Metaphor for Living

*I*n farming, the critical nature of the interrelationships among people and between people and the earth is perhaps more apparent than in any other form of human activity. The problems confronting agriculture and the problems confronting society in general share a common source — the dysfunctional nature of relationships among people and between people and the earth. The solutions to the problems of society are essentially the same as solutions to the problems of agriculture. It's just that the nature of the problems and solutions in agriculture are more easily seen and understood. Thus, farming provides a useful metaphor for living. And more important, sustainable farming provides a useful metaphor for sustainable living.

The productivity of a farm clearly depends on the health and natural fertility of the soil. The fertility of soil depends not only on its mineral and chemical composition but also upon the millions of organisms that live in the soil, in a symbiotic relationship with the roots of plants. The productivity of farms clearly depend on the health and natural vigor of plants and animals, which in turn depend on soil, water, air, and sunlight and on the biological diversity of their natural environment. Healthy soils feed healthy plants, and healthy plants feed healthy animals — including us humans who eat both plants and animals.

The profitability of a farm depends on the nature of relationships among people — between farmers and their customers and between farmers and their suppliers. A profitable farming operation must have good markets — someone somewhere must be willing and able to pay for things that farmers grow. A profitable farming operation also must have some control over its costs of production. No selling price is high enough if input suppliers simply raise their prices and absorb the farmer's profits. The economic viability of a farm clearly depends on economic relationships, which in fact, are nothing more or less, than impersonal relationships among people.

The quality of life on a farm certainly is affected by farm income, but clearly depends at least as much on quality of relationships among those who live and work on farms and between farm families and their communities. Historically, family farms have involved the whole family in important farming decisions, as well as depended on all members of the family for labor. Historically, farm families have been more isolated by geography than have non-farm families, and thus have relied more on each other for social, recreational, and emotional relationships. Likewise, many farming communities have remained isolated from the economic mainstream, making the interdependence between farm families and the social and political life of rural communities more clear. The same types of personal interdependence exist throughout society, but in farming, they have been easier to see and to understand.

The environmental, social, and economic problems confronting American agriculture today are symptoms of agricultural industrialization — specialization, standardization, and consolidation of control. The health and productivity of the soil is being destroyed by the commercial chemicals needed to support large-scale, specialized farming operations. The demise of family farms is a symptom of simplification, routinization, and mechanization of farming, which made it both possible and necessary for each farmer to farm more land and invest more capital. Get bigger or get out, they were told. As family farms failed, local businesses suffered, local schools were lost to consolidation, church pews were left empty, and rural communities withered and died. Specialization and standardization, which first led to fewer and larger farms, is now shifting control of farming to a handful of multinational corporations. Under corporate control, American agriculture might well be moved to other countries with lower land and labor costs and fewer environmental regulations. The sustainability of American agriculture is in doubt.

Those same relationships between the industrial paradigm and sustainability exist for society in general. But modern society is extremely complex and the relationships are not quite so clear. All of life, including human life, is dependent upon a healthy natural environment — water, air, sunlight, soil, and diversity of living species. Industrial systems of economic development degrade the health of the natural environment in general, just as they degrade the natural productivity of farms. Industrial systems threaten human health and well-being, as they pollute the natural environment with chemicals and other industrial wastes.

Human civilizations depend upon healthy human societies, based on inviolate principles of healthy human relationships, such as honesty, fairness, responsibility, compassion, and respect. Industrial systems, in facilitating ever-greater specialization, separate people from each other. Complex systems of markets separate buyers from sellers, consumers from producers, and corporate investors from managers. Relationships become defined by laws, rules, regulations, and contracts. Profits and growth take precedent over personal relationships and social responsibility. Exploitation of workers, consumers, and taxpayers becomes routine business practice. The degradation of American society is no different in concept from the demise of our family farms and the ecological, economic, and social decay of our rural communities. The linkages between cause and effect are just easier to see in agriculture.

The keys to building a more sustainable human society are no different in nature from the keys to building a more sustainable agriculture. Thousands of farmers all across America and around the world are finding ways to make agriculture more sustainable. Each of these *new* farmers has a unique and different story, but each shares a common vision of a more sustainable agriculture. While there are no blueprints for the new American farm, some fundamental principles are emerging.

The new farms tend to be more diversified than are conventional farms. These farmers are committed to caring for the land and protecting the natural environment. They work with nature rather than try to control or conquer nature, and nature is inherently diverse. They fit the farm to their land and climate rather than try to bend nature to fit the way they might prefer to farm. In most regions, this requires a variety of crop and animal enterprises. In some regions, however, diversity means crop rotations and cover crops. In other regions, diversity means managing livestock grazing to achieve diverse plant species or with multiple species of grazing animals. Through diversification, these new farmers substitute management for the off-farm inputs that squeeze farm profits and threaten the environment. Their farms are more economically viable, as well as more ecologically sound, because they farm in harmony with nature.

The new farmers tend to have more direct contact with their customers than do conventional farmers. Most either market their products direct to customers or market through agents who represent them with their customers. They realize that each of us value things differently, as consumers, because we have different needs and different tastes and preferences. They produce the things that their customers value most, rather than try to convince their customers to buy whatever they produce. They market to people who care where their food comes from and how it is produced — locally grown, organic, natural, humanely raised, hormone and antibiotic free — and, they receive premium prices because they produce things their customers value. Their farming operations are more economically viable, as well as ecologically sound and socially responsible.

To these new farmers, farming is as much a way of life as a way to make a living. They are "quality of life" farmers. To them, the farm is a good place to live, a good place to raise a family, and a good way to be a part of a caring community. Their quality of life objectives are at least as important as the economic objectives in carrying out their farming operations. Their farming operations reflect the things they like to do, the things they believe in, and the things they have a passion for, as much as the things that might make money. However, for many, their products are better, and their costs are less; because by following their passion, they end up doing what they do best. Most new farmers are able to earn a decent income, but more important, they have a higher quality of life because they are living a life that they love.

As these new farmers find ways to farm more sustainably, they are creating a metaphor for a more sustainable human society. If we are to sustain productivity, we must stop exploiting our natural environment. We should look again to the timeless principle of diversity in finding new means of sustaining human progress, economically and socially, while maintaining the health and integrity of our natural environment, not just in agriculture but all across society. If we are to sustain human civilization, we must stop exploiting each other. We should focus on providing people with the things they need and truly value rather than coercing and bribing people to buy ever more "cheap stuff," not just in agriculture but all across society. We must not allow our pursuit of short-run, economic self-interest to diminish our overall quality of life, neither in agriculture nor elsewhere in society. We must seek and find balance and harmony among the economic, ecological, and social to find balance and harmony among the personal, interpersonal, and spiritual dimensions of our lives.

A sustainable agriculture must be ecologically sound, economically viable, and socially responsible. The sustainability of human society must be ecologically sound, economically viable, and socially responsible. Sustainable farming is a useful metaphor for sustainable living because the critical nature of relationships among people and between people and nature are easier to see on the farm.

2002

39 | The Living Farm

Sustainable farming will require ways of thinking that are fundamentally different from the mechanistic, industrial thought processes that have dominated human thought for the past four centuries. Industrialization is the physical manifestation of a mechanistic worldview, which dates back to the seventeenth century, to the "enlightenment" and the birth of science. Rene Descartes, a Frenchman, suggested that the world worked like a large complex machine — specifically like a large clock — with many interrelated but separable parts. Sir Isaac Newton, an Englishman, built upon Descartes' ideas and developed many of the fundamental principles of modern mechanical physics.

At first, the new principles of physics were used only in dealing with "non-living things" — inanimate materials, such as water, minerals, gases — as Descartes suggested was their appropriate use. Over time, however, scientists began to use the same principles to study and to manipulate "living things," even "thinking things." Today, modern science treats all things as if they were mechanistic, including living things — plants, animals, and humans. Muscles and bones are nothing more than a complex system of levers and pulleys, the circulatory system a complicated plumbing system with pumps and valves, and the mind, a sophisticated computer with electrical circuits and connections.

This mechanistic worldview has led to the many marvels of today's world of science. It provided the conceptual foundation for the industrial era of human progress. Machines could duplicate, extend, and eventually replace the productive processes of nature. Factories could be built that would use machines, fossil energy, and human labor to transform various raw materials into useful finished products, much as nature uses plants and solar energy to transform minerals from the earth into food and fiber. People were no longer dependent on nature. They could manufacture the things they needed or wanted. They didn't have to wait for nature to provide them.

The industrial era brought many benefits. It removed much of the drudgery from day-to-day life; it challenged the then constant specter of starvation, and it suppressed diseases and extended human life. Few would willingly choose to return to a pre-industrial world. However, in the past few decades, we have begun to realize that treating *living* things as if they were *non-living* has inherent negative consequences. In fact, nearly every social ill of today can be traced to the separation of people — the destruction of family and community, the domination of the masses by the few are all consequences of a specialized, standardized, centralized industrial economy.

Nearly every environmental problem confronting society today is a consequence of people becoming separated from the land, from the earth, then treating inherently diverse and dynamic natural ecosystems as if they were specialized, inanimate machines or factories. The economic problems that today confront individually owned and operated small businesses are all direct consequences of corporate consolidation of economic power and control, which has characterized the industrial era. And, nowhere are the social, ecological, and economic problems of mechanistic thinking more evident than on American farms.

A farm is a living organism — soils, plants, animals, people, all are living, growing organs. The social, ecological, and economic problems of American agriculture today are all direct consequences of treating the soil, plants, animals, and people as if they were separable, replaceable, mechanistic parts of some sort of sophisticated "biological factory." The current "biotech craze" in the "life sciences" community is but the latest product of an outdated worldview that life is nothing more than a sophisticated mechanical process to be manipulated for economic gain. But a farm is a living organism made up of microorganisms, plants, and animals. And farmers are breathing, thinking, caring, living beings. Solutions to the current problems of American agriculture will require new ways of thinking — a new "living" worldview.

Living things are "self-making" — they have the capacity to grow and reproduce; dead things cannot. Machines are manmade; they are designed to perform specific functions to achieve a specific purpose. They may be well maintained, but all machines eventually wear out. Worn out machines must be discarded and may or may not be replaced. Living things are conceived, born, germinate, hatch, or otherwise come to life. As they grow and mature, they learn to perform various functions to fulfill their purpose in life. They may be well nurtured, but all living things eventually die. Before they die, however, living things have the capacity to reproduce — to regenerate their communities and their species.

Because they are self-making, living things are dynamic; they are ever changing, even though the pattern of a living thing, its DNA, remains unchanged throughout its life. A human is a human at all stages of life — whether it's a bouncing baby, a strong mature adult, or a feeble "senior citizen," it's the *same* human, but ever changing in physical structure and appearance.

Living things are also holistic. If the various parts of our bodies were surgically separated and laid side by side on an operating table, our life, the essence of who we are, obviously would have been destroyed. Our life would be gone. Dividing an elephant into a dozen pieces obviously doesn't result in a dozen little elephants. A living organism is more than the "sum of its parts," living organisms are inseparable, holistic.

Farms are living organisms; they are regenerative, dynamic, and holistic. They are not machines or factories. If farming systems are to be sustainable, our ways of thinking about farming must reflect their regenerative, dynamic, and holistic nature. We must have the courage and wisdom to abandon the old, mechanistic worldview and adopt new, organismic ways of thinking about farming.

A farm represents a purposeful "organization" of resources — land, labor, capital, and management. The purpose of a sustainable farm must reflect its multidimensional nature, its economic, ecological, and social dimensions. However, a sustainable farm is not multipurpose. Its purpose is holistic, and thus, is not separable into sub-purposes. A farm cannot make more money, for example, without affecting the land and the relationships among people on the farm and in the community. Nor can a farm reduce soil loss or protect water quality without affecting its economic performance and its contributions to society. So, every decision made on the farm has economic, ecological, and social implications. Every farm thus should be organized with a definite purpose in mind that considers its economic, ecological, and social potential. An essential aspect of the purpose of all sustainable farms is *permanence.*

The principles by which a sustainable farm is operated constitute its conceptual DNA. Just as DNA defines the nature of a living organism, principles define the nature of a farm. The principles followed in managing a farm will determine whether it is capable of fulfilling its purpose. The number of principles should be sufficient to insure that, if followed, the purpose will be fulfilled, but not more than necessary to ensure the purpose. As humans, we want all of the genetic material necessary to ensure that we are healthy humans, but we don't want anything extra. The fundamental principles of sustainable farming are those of economic viability, ecological integrity, and social responsibility. The specific principles by which individual farms are managed will be different, reflecting the uniqueness of the farm, the farmer, and the "community." But to be sustainable, the principles of a farm must be both necessary and sufficient to ensure permanence — sustainability.

The definition of purpose and principles represents the "conception" of a farm. Once conceived, the farm is free to "come to life" — to emerge, to grow, to mature, to regenerate, and to evolve. Creating a living farm is not like building a factory, to be used, worn out and discarded or rebuilt. A living farm is conceived, comes to life, grows, matures, reproduces, and evolves — like a living organism. As farming takes from the soil, it rebuilds the soil; as it earns money, it reinvests money; as it demands personal commitment, it contributes to quality of life. It is dynamic, ever changing in its structure and appearance, but is ever constant in its purpose and principles. Farms also may evolve forward into marketing and distribution or backward into production of inputs. As a farm grows and matures, the farming practices, methods, and enterprises may change, but the farm that remains true to its economic, ecological, and social principles will remain true to its purpose and will be sustainable.

Old farmers eventually must be replaced by younger farmers; sick and worn down farms may be nursed back to life and health. But life in the soil and life on the farm must go on. If we allow *living* farms to die, they cannot be restored to life. A farm is not a machine that can be restarted or a factory that can be rebuilt. Once a life is gone, it is gone forever. Farming sustainably requires a different way of thinking about farming. We must have the wisdom to reject the old, mechanistic worldview, and the courage to challenge the conventional wisdom that a farm can be run like a factory. We must conceive new systems of *living* farms that will be capable of sustaining a regenerative, dynamic, holistic, living, human society.

2002

40 | A Question of Boundaries

Good fences make good neighbors," so the old saying goes. There are fewer opportunities for conflicts if you keep your livestock out of your neighbors' fields, and they keep theirs out of yours; the same goes for keeping pets in your own yard. But good fences also have gates and are easy to "talk over." Fences that separate people completely "don't make good neighbors," they create isolation, distrust, and dissention. Fences define boundaries. Good boundaries keep some things in and some things out, but also must let some things pass through.

I recall learning about good boundaries in a high school science class — they were called semi-permeable membranes. The walls of living cells let some things pass through, but keep other things in and out — so they are called "semi"-permeable. If the cells in our body either were permeable or non-permeable, rather than semi-permeable, they would not support life. If they didn't keep anything in, we would dry up. If they didn't let anything out, we would blow up. If they weren't semi-permeable, they wouldn't be able to retain moisture or minerals; they wouldn't be able to metabolize food, release energy, or eliminate waste. We would die. All living things are made up of cells defined by semi-permeable boundaries.

This principle of good boundaries applies to many other aspects of life. Living organisms are defined by boundaries — skin, bark, leaf surface, scales — which give them form and identity. As with cells, the boundaries of organisms must be semi-permeable or selective with respect to what they allow to pass through and what they keep in or out.

Some boundaries are social or cultural rather than physical. Families are defined by boundaries. The relationships we have with people within our family are different from those with people outside our family. Members of healthy families have relationships with people both within and outside of their families, but the relationships must be selective. Communities have boundaries, although typically less well defined than for families. In healthy communities, people within the community share relationships that are different from their relationships with people outside the community. States and nations are defined by political boundaries, and again, the borders of states and nations are semi-permeable or selective, by design and by necessity. We Americans need to relate to people in other nations, but we purposefully relate to other Americans differently than we relate to those of other nations.

Without personal, cultural, and political boundaries human civilization, as we know it, could not exist. Without civilized human behavior, life on earth might well cease to exist. Good boundaries are necessary for life.

One of the fundamental characteristics of living things — plants, animals, insects, bacteria, and so on — is their ability to recreate and to reproduce themselves, and thus, to create new boundaries. In fact, the natural tendency of all living systems is toward the creation of greater biological diversity, meaning more different identities and forms of things, and thus, more boundaries. For example, after a field has been stripped of all vegetation, the first life to return to a field likely will be a single, or possibly a few, species of "weeds." The weeds will mature, reproduce, and die, but their rotted residue will create a favorable environment for other plant species. As the succession of regeneration processes continues, an increasing diversity of plant species will create a favorable habitat for an increasing diversity of microorganism, insect, and animal species. And this increasing diversity of form and structure is defined by a multitude of new boundaries.

Unlike living things, the natural tendency for "non-living things" is toward the dissolution or destruction of boundaries. In physics, this is called a natural tendency toward "entropy." Entropy is defined as "the ultimate state reached in degradation of matter and energy of the universe; a state of inert uniformity of component elements; absence of form, pattern, hierarchy, or differentiation." Entropy is characterized by the complete absence of boundaries.

In the definition of entropy, "degradation of energy and matter" refers to the fact that boundaries are destroyed by the release of energy from matter, and that new energy is required to rebuild boundaries and restore energy. For example, when an oak log is burned, energy, in the form of heat, is released from the wood, and the structure of the wood is turned to ashes. The boundaries that once defined the structure of the log are destroyed through the releasing of energy. In this case, energy from the sun helps grow new trees, which offsets the energy lost to entropy. The human body converts food to energy by a similar process of digesting or breaking down the structure of the things we eat. In both cases, the energy consumed is renewable because new energy can be captured from the sun by other living organisms to offset entropy.

Whenever energy is released from matter, some energy must be used to restore the boundaries and restore energy, leaving less "useful energy" than before. Lacking a new infusion of energy from "outside" — as from the sun — systems slowly lose their ability to restore boundaries, and thus, slowly lose their ability to store and release energy. This is the essence of entropy — the degradation of energy and matter, as systems lose their form, structure, and diversity through the destruction of boundaries.

This may all sound a bit esoteric; however, the concept of entropy is equally relevant to cultural, political, and economic systems. The dissolution of boundaries among cultures increases the efficiency of social and political processes, releasing the energy previously bound by cultural constraints. The dissolution of political boundaries, likewise, releases the energy bound by conflicting laws, regulations, and other political constraints. The dissolution of cultural and political boundaries removes obstacles of economic specialization, standardization, and consolidation, thus allowing maximum productivity and economic efficiency. Thus, strong social and economic incentives exist to remove all cultural and political boundaries.

On farms, we have seen tremendous gains in productivity and economic efficiency through the removal of boundaries. Farmers removed fences that had separated fields, as they moved toward more mechanized and standardized systems of farming. The diversity of crops and livestock enterprises that once defined the structure of typical family farms was abandoned to achieve greater specialization. The "landscapes" of many farms were left without form, pattern, hierarchy, or differentiation.

These new "more efficient" farming methods have allowed farms to become larger, through consolidation, removing the boundaries of ownership and identity that once defined different farms within communities. As farms became larger, farmers reached beyond the boundaries of the local communities to market their products and purchase their inputs because it was "more efficient" to do so. The economic boundaries of communities were blurred, if not erased.

This transformation, this industrialization of agriculture, has resulted in tremendous gains in agricultural productivity and economic efficiency. As with industrialization in general, it has released tremendous stocks of stored energy that were constrained by the boundaries that once defined different fields, enterprises, farms, and farming communities. The boundaries have been removed and the energy has been released. But once the stored energy has been used up, where will we get new energy?

Industrialization is a "non-living" system. It destroys boundaries in order to extract the stored energy from land, water, air, plants, animals, and people. However, it has no means of restoring boundaries, no means of recreating matter or restoring energy, and thus, no means of renewing sources of energy for the future. The amount of fossil energy — fuel, fertilizer, pesticides, electricity — used by today's industrial farming operations exceed the amount of solar energy they are able to capture from the sun. Industrial systems trend toward entropy — toward degradation of matter and energy; toward a state of inert uniformity; toward an absence of form, pattern, hierarchy, or differentiation. A lifeless desert is about as close to entropy as most of us have seen. It is without form, pattern, hierarchy, or differentiation — without boundaries. Such will be the ultimate result of agricultural industrialization.

Entropy is not just a physical phenomenon. The consolidation of production into fewer and larger units and the consolidation of control under fewer and larger corporate entities are examples of organizational entropy. "Free trade," defined as the removal of all national restraints to trade, exemplifies economic entropy. The forming of economic unions and the resulting loss of cultural identity reflect a loss of form, pattern, and diversity. All of these things result in increased efficiency because they release the energy constrained by organizational, economic, and cultural boundaries. The problem is not that energy is released, but that nothing is done to renew and restore it.

Sustainable systems, on the other hand, are living systems — they are self-renewing, reproductive, regenerative systems of production. Living systems must have boundaries — not barriers that keep everything in or out, but semi-permeable boundaries that keep some things in and keep some things out. Living systems are dynamic. Boundaries are destroyed, through use and decay, but boundaries also are restored through regrowth and reproduction. Living systems are able to capture energy from the sun, either directly or indirectly, which offsets the natural entropy brought about by the inevitable death and decay. Living systems tend toward greater diversity of form, structure, and pattern as they create new boundaries. The process of energy renewal and regeneration, this natural tendency of living systems, is our only means of offsetting the natural tendency of dead systems toward entropy.

We will need to build lots of new "good fences" to restore the sustainability to agriculture. We don't need fences that create isolation, distrust, and dissention, but fences with gates that are easy to "talk over." Sustainable agriculture is a holistic, diverse, dynamic, interdependent, "living" process. Sustainability requires good boundaries.

2002

41 | Agricultural Sustainability & the New Jubilee

I *t is not my intention to promote any particular religious view-point or even to promote religion. But sustainability is undeni-ably rooted in spirituality, as I have written many times before. I believe religion is a legitimate means, while certainly not the only means, of expressing the spirituality of sustainability.*

A sustainable farm is a living organism, as I have also written many times before. A farm's sustaining ability depends on the self-renewing and regenerative capacity of its living systems — its soils, plants, animals, and people. Living things, by nature, must have periods of rest in order to renew their physical structures, reproduce themselves, and evolve to accommodate changes in their environment.

Natural ecosystems have natural sustaining ability; they were created that way by nature. Economic and social systems, on the other hand, are creations of people; they are whatever we choose to make them. Unfortunately, the economic and social systems that dominate America and much of the rest of the world today are not created in the image of nature; they have no natural capacity for rest, renewal, regeneration, evo-lution. Thus, the sustainable farmer must be guided by principles different from those that guide his or her more conventional farming neighbors.

The dominant economic system of today was designed to extract and exploit both natural and human resources; it has no inherent capacity for rest or for renewal and restoration of the resources it uses up in the production process. For example, publicly held corporate organizations, which dominate today's economy, have no natural life cycle of birth, maturity, and death; they are designed to live and to exploit continuously, forever. The dominant social system of today facilitates the pursuit of individual, material self-interests; it has no inherent capacity for renewal and regeneration of the social connections it inevitably destroys nor does it tolerate idleness or rest. It places no value on connectedness; it reflects the belief that society functions best when everyone takes care of themselves and expects others, including those of future generations, to do likewise. It respects no natural limitations of nature or humanity.

Admittedly, many members of society support various actions, both personally and politically, to mitigate the negative ecological and social consequences of their individual pursuit of self-interests. However, the dominant economic and social systems of today lack the capacities of living natural systems for rest, renewal, and regeneration. If we are to sustain a desirable quality of human life on earth, our economic and social systems must be recreated in the image of nature. We must create a living society and a living economy with built-in capacities for rest, renewal, regeneration. The biblical concept of jubilee could provide a philosophical cornerstone for such a new living economy and new living society.

In the Bible, the people of Israel were instructed by God to proclaim a year of jubilee every fifty years. "Consecrate the fiftieth year and proclaim liberty throughout the land to all its inhabitants. It shall be a jubilee for you; each one of you is to return to his family property and each to his own clan" (Leviticus 25:10). During the year of jubilee, all people were instructed to rest the land, to release the slaves, to forgive all debts, and to redistribute the land. The year of jubilee was to be a year of rest, renewal, regeneration, and new beginnings — for the people and for the land.

The biblical admonition for periodic rest of the land reflects an understanding of the necessity for ecological integrity in creating and maintaining sustainable systems. Natural systems have the inherent capacity for sustainability, but they must be allowed times of restoration, renewal, regeneration interspersed with times of use and productivity. Sustainable farmers know they must rotate their fields among various crops, some of which allow the soil to rest, renew, and regenerate between periods of production for harvest. Periodic times of jubilee, of renewal for the whole farm, including the farm family, might even further enhance agricultural sustainability.

The biblical admonition for periodic release of slaves reflects an understanding of the necessity for social responsibility in creating and maintaining sustainable systems. Slaves of biblical times are analogous to farm workers of today. Sustainable social systems must provide opportunities for people, including farmers, to reach their full potential for leading productive, useful, rewarding lives — regardless of their present circumstances. Sustainable farmers must be given periodic opportunities to relearn and rethink their work and their life. Sustainability requires periodic introspection and forgiveness of self and others for past errors in thoughts, words, and actions.

A socially responsible agriculture requires equity of opportunity — all who choose to farm must be given an opportunity to realize their full potential for contribution and self-fulfillment. Today's "agricultural slaves" are the seasonal farm workers and contract producers who find themselves at the mercy of corporate agribusiness. Thus, seasonal farm workers, contract farmers, and other wanna-be farmers must be given opportunities, support, and encouragement to "free themselves" from their current dependence and to become independent, responsible stewards of the land. Periodic times of jubilee, of unique opportunity for beginning farmers, might further enhance agricultural sustainability.

The biblical admonition for periodic remission of debts reflects an understanding of the necessity for economic viability in creating and maintaining sustainable systems. A sustainable system must be capable of economic renewal and regeneration. Sustainable farmers know they must earn enough to be able to replace whatever rusts, rots, or wears out. Thus, they minimize their investment in machinery, equipment, and commercial inputs and maximize their reliance on management of renewable human and natural resources. However, given today's imperfect knowledge of sustainable farming, even the best of farmers may not be able to weather times of extreme economic adversity, which often defy either anticipation or control.

Many conventional farmers who would like to make the transition to sustainable farming may be too far in debt to defy the demands from their creditors that they continue to farm conventionally — until they lose their farms. Many farmers who are currently in the transition process, from conventional to sustainable farming, may be particularly vulnerable to economic adversity. Periodic times of jubilee, of conditional forgiveness of farm debts, might speed the transition to sustainability.

Finally, the biblical admonition of redistribution of land reflects an understanding of the necessity for overall ecological, economic, and social renewal and regeneration in creating and maintaining sustainable systems. Human societies and economies must continually renew, regenerate, and evolve over time to accommodate our ever-expanding knowledge of an ever-changing natural environment. Likewise, sustainable farms must be continually renewed and regenerated — including the farmer and the farm family, as well as the farm.

Farm families do not naturally regenerate themselves, as farm children are often prepared for and encouraged to seek their future in non-farm occupations. Even when new generations within farm families stay on the farm, the new generation may not be willing or able to accept the stewardship responsibilities of farming. In reality, the land does not "belong" to the farmer; the farmer is simply the steward or caretaker of the land. The farmer has a conditional right to use the land and to benefit economically; but that right carries with it the moral and ethical responsibility to leave the land as good as it was found. These limited use rights may be passed from one generation to the next within families, but along with the rights must pass the associated stewardship responsibilities. Some new socially acceptable means must be found for redistributing farmland from those who are unwilling or unable to accept the responsibility of land stewardship to those who are willing and able to farm the land sustainably.

I am not suggesting that times of jubilee be declared by means of some government fiat or religious decree. I am suggesting that government farm policies should be redirected from supporting the current extractive and exploitation systems of agricultural production to supporting, instead, the transition to a more sustainable agriculture. I am also suggesting that the religious concept of jubilee — of periodic rest for land and people, new opportunities for beginning farmers, forgiveness of debts, and redistribution of land — are fundamental principles for serious consideration in reformulating agricultural policies.

Perhaps even more important, however, the concept of jubilee can help guide individual farmers toward a more desirable quality of life. Farmers need not wait for changes in public policies. Farmers with a sense of spirituality, with a commitment to finding ways to farm and live sustainably in harmony with the higher order of things, can declare a time of jubilee on their farms any time they choose. They can declare a day, a week, or a year of rest — a time to think about farming and about life. They can find ways to free themselves from dependent relationships and free others who have become too dependent upon them. They can find ways to reduce, if not eliminate, their debts and ways to help others repay debts owed to them. They can find ways to ensure that their land is passed on to a new generation of stewards, who will leave the land as good as they found it for the generation that follows them.

Farmers can enhance the sustainability of their farms and the quality of their lives — personally, socially, and spiritually. They can declare their own new jubilee, and they can do it any time they choose.

2004

42 | Sustainability & Biotechnology

iotechnology is touted by some as the key to sustainable agriculture. However, I fail to see that biotechnology has anything positive to contribute to the sustainability of agriculture in America or elsewhere in the world. Advocates of biotechnology label skeptics such as me as uniformed alarmists or as romantic idealists who long for a world long past. If we don't embrace every new technology that is developed, they conclude we must have some irrational fear of the future. After all, the universities, the government, and the big corporations are all promoting biotechnology as a shining new star in the crown for human ingenuity. What rights do we ordinary people have to oppose this new technology? What rights do we have to question the wisdom of the intellectually, economically, and politically powerful?

First, we have every right to question the scientific community because the science currently used in biotechnology simply is not appropriate for the study of living things. Today's science of biotechnology is based on a mechanistic worldview developed more than four-hundred years ago, which assumes the earth and everything on it operates a lot like a machine. Most scientists believe living things ultimately are nothing more than sophisticated machines with interchangeable and replaceable parts. Up to now, we have simply lacked the technical ability to build, redesign, repair, and replace living things. Biotechnology promises to give us that ability.

But living things are not machines. Even the early scientists recognized that the mechanical model was not appropriate for living things — particularly not for thinking things. A fundamental difference is that living things are "self-making" — they renew and reproduce themselves. They renew their bodies as they grow, continually respond to their changing environment, and eventually mature and reproduce before they die. Machines are built; they function, eventually wear out, and are discarded. Machines can't remake themselves.

The difference between dealing with dead and living things is like the difference between kicking a football and kicking a dog. When you kick a football, you can calculate precisely what is going to happen, if you are smart enough to take into account such things as foot speed, angle of impact, temperature, wind speed, and so on. But when you kick a dog, you don't know what's going to happen. The dog may lie down and whimper, yelp and run, stand and growl, bite your foot, or wait until your back is turned and take a hunk out of your backside. Genetic engineering is a lot more like kicking a dog than a football. Scientists just don't know what will happen.

Scientists agree that the expression of a gene within a living organism depends upon its context — its relationship with other genes, which define the organism as a whole. Thus, when genetic engineers insert a new gene into a living organism, the context of every other gene in the organism has been changed. They may have a pretty good idea of how the new gene will express itself, but they have no way of knowing how the expression of any other genes may be changed, particularly in some future generation of the organism.

Since the responses to this genetic tinkering are inherently uncertain, the risks associated with biotechnology cannot be estimated, regardless of claims to the contrary. In order to assess risk, one must at least have a reasonable estimate of the distribution of possible future outcomes or occurrences. In other words, we must have a reasonable estimate of the chances of something bad happening, regardless of whether the odds are one-in-two, one-in-a-hundred, or one-in-a-million. With biotechnology, scientists don't have a clue. It might be relatively safe or it may be deadly. We just don't know.

Under such conditions of uncertainty, we should practice the "precautionary principle." A new product should not be approved unless there is "compelling evidence" that it is safe and promises important public benefits. In addition, the burden of evidence of safety and effectiveness should be the responsibility of the one seeking approval and not the responsibility of the public. The Europeans have applied this principle to Genetically Modified Organisms, and thus far, have rejected them. We apply the precautionary principle to medicine. We also should proceed with caution in all matters related to biotechnology.

Advocates say that genetic engineering is essentially the same as earlier work with genetic selection. Once again, they ignore the fact that they are working with living organisms. Transgenic organisms, such as strawberries with a fish gene inserted to improve frost resistance, could not possibly have occurred through natural reproduction. In nature, genetic materials are not normally exchanged across the boundaries that separate different genera. It happens only rarely and is referred to as a genetic aberration. Nature also places limits on the speed with which genetic change can take place within species. Genetic engineering ignores all such natural boundaries.

Nuclear engineering is the only previous venture in science that is even remotely similar in nature to genetic engineering. Nuclear energy is created by tinkering with the atom, a fundamental building block of matter. Genetic engineers are tinkering with genes, the fundamental building blocks of life. Humanity has been dealing with the unanticipated "fallout" of nuclear energy ever since the first atom bomb was exploded, and there is no end to the variety of possible nuclear crises in sight. A primary difference between nuclear fallout and genetic fallout is that living things reproduce and spread on their own. There is no way to put the *genetic genie* back in the bottle.

We also have a right to question the economics of biotechnology because the same corporations that brought us agricultural pesticides are now bringing us biotechnology. These same corporations made billions of dollars selling farmers pesticides, and now they want to make billions of dollars selling farmers biotech replacements for those pesticides — many of which are no longer effective. These firms introduced commercial pesticides fifty years ago without knowing the risks, because they were dealing with complex living organisms and couldn't possibly have known the risk. But at the time, no one could prove that they weren't safe, so we allowed farmers to use them. Only decades later did we decide to ban whole classes of pesticides as threats to human health and the natural environment. The sad fact is that these corporations know far less about the consequences of biotechnology today than they knew about the threats of pesticides fifty years ago. They are interested in profits, not protection of the environment or feeding the world's hungry people.

These corporations claim that biotechnology will be needed to feed the growing world population. However, they insist on patenting their genetic discoveries. The only reason for a patent is to grant an exclusive right to make a profit from a discovery. If we were really interested in feeding the world, biotechnology would be developed with public research dollars and discoveries would be free for all to use without charge. The give-away patent for "golden rice" to fight malnutrition and promises to develop bio-vaccines to fight disease are nothing more than public relations and marketing gimmicks. Any future public benefits of biotechnology will go to those who are able to pay the corporate price, and that will not include the poor and starving people of the world. If we were really serious about feeding the hungry of the world, we could do it today. There is plenty of money and plenty of know how, but there is a serious lack of will to share either. Biotechnology won't change the human heart, at least not for the better, and therefore, biotechnology won't feed the poor.

We also have a right to question the politics of biotechnology. The agricultural establishment supports biotech because it has been sold as the future of farming. In one sense, the hype is true. Biotechnology may eventually bring an end to real farming. Biotechnology will result in the same type of corporate control of crops and livestock as we now see in the poultry and pork industries. Eventually, farmers who do not have verifiable, *approved genetics* will find that they have no markets. In order to gain market access, they will have to produce approved varieties, which can be obtained only through contractual arrangements with the patent holders — the biotech corporations. Farmers will become contractors, at best, and in most cases will be little more than corporate hired hands.

We also have a responsibility to question the politics of biotech because it is draining scarce public dollars away from use in meeting the real challenges of the future of agriculture. Ultimately, we must have a sustainable system of food production or humanity simply will not survive. Thousands of farmers around the globe are working to build such a system, but they are forced to do it pretty much on their own. Successful examples of sustainable farmers around the globe serve as proof that we don't need biotechnology to feed the world, we just need a lot more people who understand how to work with nature rather than against it. While our public universities and agencies are spending billions of taxpayers' dollars to subsidize giant multinational corporations, these innovative, creative farmers are working, with very little outside help, to create the real future of agriculture.

We have perhaps a fifty-year window of opportunity to develop a system of food and fiber production that is economically viable, ecologically sound, and socially responsible. Biotechnology fails all three tests of sustainability. We have every right to question those who advocate biotechnology as the future of agriculture and of humanity.

2001

43 | The Case Against Patenting Life

*P*ercy Schmeiser is a hero. He sacrificed a good bit of his life and risked everything he owned in pursuit of a worthy cause. In the end, he lost, but he lost while *daring greatly*. As Teddy Roosevelt once said of the "man who is in the arena . . . if he fails while daring greatly, he knows that his place shall never be among those cold and timid souls who know neither victory nor defeat." I visited with Percy a few times during his long, costly ordeal, as he traveled the continent and the world, making his case against genetic patenting. I found him to be a brave man of noble qualities, capable of great deeds — a hero.

Percy Schmeiser is the Canadian farmer who was sued by Monsanto for planting canola seed containing Roundup Ready genes on his farm. Monsanto admitted he had not bought the seed from them, but somehow Monsanto's genes found their way onto Percy's farm. In an early court ruling, the judge declared the source of the seeds to be irrelevant. Monsanto owned the genetic patent, thus the canola belonged to Monsanto, and Percy had no legal right to harvest or replant the seeds. Percy defended his basic right to save and to replant seeds grown on his farm. He continued his fight all the way to the Canadian Supreme Court, where at last he was able to challenge the constitutionality of genetic patenting in general.

He lost, but only by a split decision of five to four and the court awarded no monetary damages or compensation for legal fees to Monsanto. Percy never intended to make a profit from Roundup Ready canola; he only wanted to make a statement. A complete explanation of the court decision, including Percy's response, can be found at *www.percyschmeiser.com*. So patenting of living organisms was deemed legal in Canada, as it has been in the United States. But the issue is far from being finally resolved.

A patent is a legal document granted by the government giving an inventor the exclusive right to make, use, and sell an invention for a specified number of years. A patent, in effect, gives the inventor a legal monopoly. In the U.S., patents are granted for inventions and significant improvements in machines, chemical compounds, manufactured items, and industrial processes. Special patents have also been granted for "invention or discovery and asexual reproduction of living organisms," but the legitimacy of all such special patents remains in doubt.

In general, to qualify for a patent, an invention or discovery must meet three basic tests. First, it must be "novel," meaning it did not previously exist. Second, it must be "non-obvious," meaning it is significantly different from existing technology. Finally, it must be "useful," meaning it cannot be used for an illegal or immoral purpose. Historically, however, some types of discoveries have been deemed not patentable. For example, no one can obtain a patent on a law of nature or a scientific principle, even if he or she is the first one to discover it. For example, Isaac Newton could not have obtained a patent on the laws of gravity, and Albert Einstein could not have patented his famous formula, $E=mc^2$.

Previous judges apparently have accepted the premise that living organisms are essentially the same in nature as machines, material compositions, manufactured items, and industrial processes, to which patent laws obviously were meant to apply. Plants of unique appearance or functional traits, achieved through selective plant breeding, apparently have been treated as analogous to inventions in patent laws. In addition, patents have been granted for plants with distinctive functional traits "invented" through genetic engineering, through manipulation of genetic materials. In court interpretations of patent laws, the manipulation of living processes apparently has been treated essentially the same as combining chemicals, minerals, or gasses, or assembling the parts of a machine.

However, important questions remain as to whether patenting of living organisms *should* be allowable — even under existing patent laws. An organism may be novel, at least in function or appearance, non-obvious, and useful, but it still may not be legitimately patentable. The fundamental questions are, first, is a living organism a discovery, rather than an invention? And second, if is it a discovery, is it a discovery of a principle, rather than a process or product? Apparently, Isaac Newton could not have patented the law of gravity because he didn't create it; he discovered it, and the uniqueness of his discovery was the *principle* of gravity — rather than the *process* or *product* of gravity. His discovery of gravity was non-obvious, novel, and useful, but the *principles* of gravity were not invented by Newton, and thus, not patentable. A similarly strong case can be made against the patenting of living organisms.

The discovery that one plant, when cross-fertilized with another, will produce offspring of distinctive appearance or functionality is very different from the manufacturing of a plant with this same distinctiveness. Even if the plant breeder could describe and explain the process by which the new plant was created, the breeder did not create the new plant, or the process by which it was created. The plant created itself according to the principles of nature. Although Newton could describe and explain the laws of gravity, he could not create the force that pulled the apple to the ground; it was pulled by the attraction of the earth. A discovery of how nature works, even if it leads to reasonably accurate predictions of novel, non-obvious, useful outcomes, is not an invention of a mechanism; it is a discovery of principles.

Even the so-called genetically engineered plants and animals are nothing more than the results of discoveries concerning how nature reacts to genetic manipulations. The genetic materials used in these manipulations were not manufactured; they were discovered in nature. And the organisms within which the foreign genetic materials are implanted were not manufactured; they were discovered. And most important of all, the reactions of an organism to the manipulation of its genetic makeup are reactions controlled purely by the principles of nature, rather than by the genetic engineer. Genetic engineers simply discover principles by which plants react to manipulation and nature's principles are not patentable.

An important and critical distinction between invention of a *mechanism* and the discovery of a *principle* is that principles cannot be controlled by those who discover them. An inventor of a process or mechanism can decide whether to produce his or her invention and can cease production whenever it is no longer considered useful. The principles and functions of organisms, on the other hand, exist before their discovery and continue to function afterwards, regardless of the actions of the discoverer. The forces of gravity and energy existed before Newton and Einstein and will continue to exist in the future, regardless. The implications of their discoveries were many and varied, but completely beyond their control. And the ultimate implications of Monsanto's genetic manipulations are completely beyond Monsanto's control.

The unique and unchanging nature of DNA, at first might seem to support the patenting of genetically modified organisms. The genetic novelty of a modified organism persists, and thus it is controllable during the life span of the organism. So, if a unique genetic code, a unique arrangement and assortment of genes, is achieved through genetic engineering, the uniqueness of the code presumably could be controlled. However, control of the assortment or arrangement of genes does not necessarily imply control of the functionality of the organism. Even if the specific function of interest — such as herbicide resistance — is verified as controllable and replicable, it is impossible to control the ultimate consequences of a new genetic assortment or arrangement for the organism as a whole, and most certainly, for its offspring.

The DNA of each living organism goes through a unique "unfolding" process, which in the absence of external influences might completely define the organism. But in reality, this "unfolding" is affected by a multitude of factors, which serve to make each living organism unique, regardless of its DNA. Some basic traits, such as color of eyes or hair in humans, may be genetically predictable, but the makeup of each individual reflects not just its DNA, but also the ever-changing environment in which it comes to life and continues to grow. I have identical twin daughters; they have the same DNA. Same eye color, same hair color, but they were very different at birth and even more different at maturity. I didn't make my daughters; they made themselves, and they made themselves unique — as will their children, and all children of future generations.

A living organism is a creation of nature, not an invention of humans. Humans cannot make living things, because all living things *make* themselves. Humans cannot control living things because they constantly *remake* themselves according to principles beyond human control. Living things continually grow, reproduce, and evolve into new and uniquely different individuals — their own individuals. Thus, the discovery of novel, nonobvious, useful principles of life must be considered as part of the public domain, accessible to all and for the benefit of all. No one should be allowed to patent life, to be granted a monopoly on life; it just doesn't make sense.

An old Native American chief responding to his warriors, who seeing the futility of their war against the "white man," asked why they should continue to fight, said, "ultimately we will not be judged by the battles we win or lose, but by the battles we choose to fight." Ultimately, Percy Schmeiser, the hero, will be judged by the battle he chose to fight.

2004

44 | The Case for Common Sense

American farmers have been told they must specialize, mechanize, and manage their farms like a business; it's the logical, reasonable thing to do. But this logic and reason has led to fewer farms, larger farms, and increasingly, to corporate control of farming. Being logical and reasonable has brought the demise of family farms and now threatens the food security of the nation. Maybe it's time to try something else. Maybe it's time for farmers to rely on their common sense.

Our common sense is our insight into the true nature of things — into what Plato referred to as "pure knowledge." Plato argued, around 400 BC, that one can never gain pure knowledge through observation. Anything that can be observed is always changing, he said, but pure knowledge never changes. He argued that we observe only imperfect examples of the true "form" of things — "form" being the order or architecture of pure knowledge. We can observe examples of "form," and we can visualize "form" in our minds through intelligent insight. However, we can never actually observe "form" — or the true order of things — because it is intangible and exists only in the abstract.

Pure knowledge exists at a higher level and thus constitutes a "higher order of things." This higher order is the part of the constant reality of the universe. We can see this higher order reflected in the world around us and in the lives of other people. However, our observations have meaning only because we may have some intuitive understanding of the true order from which things emanate. We can never gain an understanding of this higher order through observation because we can observe only imperfect examples. Instead, true understanding must come about by other means — means which may be referred to as intelligent insight, informed intuition, or better yet, "common sense."

Science, on the other hand, is based on logic and reason — not on insight and intuition. Today's science has evolved from philosophies of more than four hundred years ago. Rene Descartes, Isaac Newton, John Locke, and others of that time, hypothesized that the world worked like a big, complex machine, with many intricate and interconnected parts. They reasoned that everything that happens, every effect, must have a discernable cause. Thus, if we formulate appropriate hypotheses concerning cause and effect relationships, and if we design appropriate experiments or observations, we can find the cause of every effect and thus acquire knowledge and understanding. The thinkers of this "age of reason" laid the conceptual foundation for today's dominant notions of science.

Many scientists today believed that through logic, reason, and scientific observation, we can discover "truth" — we can find "true knowledge." Many scientists today reject anything that cannot be "proven" empirically, through observation or experiment, as irrational superstition. If you can't prove it, it simply is not true.

In relying on our common sense, we need not reject science as the only means of gaining knowledge or understanding of the things around us. But we must reject the proposition that there is only one way of knowing or understanding. Thomas Huxley, a noted English botanist, once wrote, "All truth, in the long run, is only common sense clarified." Albert Einstein wrote, "The whole of science is nothing more than a refinement of everyday thinking." We must use science to "clarify and refine" our common sense, but not allow science to replace it. We must be willing to challenge the conventional wisdom that science is the key to all knowledge with a more enlightened concept of science that respects common sense as our only source of "pure knowledge."

Conventional wisdom is something fundamentally different from common sense — although the two are sometimes mistakenly used interchangeably. Both may represent widely held opinions, but the sources of those opinions are quite different. Conventional wisdom, like science, is rooted in logic and reason — in conclusions drawn from experimentation and observation. Sometimes the logic and reasoning are faulty, and thus so are the conclusions. But even more important, "pure knowledge" can never be observed — it exists only in the abstract.

Common sense is something that we know to be true, regardless of whether we have experienced or observed it ourselves or have been informed of it by others. Conventional wisdom may include some things that make common sense. However, things "make sense" to us only if we somehow know they are true — only if the truth of it is validated by the spiritual or metaphysical part of us rather than by the logical or reasoning part of us. Some people choose to deny their spirituality, thus deny their common sense, and instead rely solely on logic and reason. But, we all have access to common sense because it is something we possess in common. But, we are each free to use or not use it.

When the framers of the Declaration of Independence wrote, "We hold these truths to be self-evident, that all men are created equal, that they are endowed by their Creator with certain unalienable Rights, that among these are Life, Liberty, and the pursuit of Happiness," they had no scientific basis for such an assertion. These truths were not derived by logic and reason, and this statement certainly did not represent conventional wisdom in those days. The truth of this statement was something they felt in their souls. They were relying on their common sense.

There is no logical, rational reason to accept the Golden Rule: do unto others, as you would have them do unto you. Yet it is a part of almost every organized religion and every enduring philosophy in the history of the world. It's just common sense. When Thomas Paine wrote of "the rights of man," and Jimmy Carter talked of "basic human rights," they were not relying on exhaustive scientific experiments. They relied instead on the common sense of humanity. Common sense comes to all of us from somewhere beyond our body and mind — from the spiritual part of us. We are not able to see the realm of the higher order of things, with our eyes or even our mind; we are only able to glimpse it through our soul. We all have access to it, but we must open our hearts and our minds to receive it. And we must accept its reality.

Our common sense today tells us something is fundamentally wrong in American agriculture. We are told we shouldn't be concerned about farm financial problems. Periodic farm crises are just normal economic adjustments, and the free-market ultimately works for the good of all, so they say. We are told we shouldn't be concerned about the natural environment, that we have no proof we are damaging the natural ecosystem, and after all, we can find a technological fix for any ecological problem. We are told we shouldn't be concerned about what is happening to family farms and rural communities, rural people want the same things urban people want, and thus they must eventually give up their rural ways of life. But, our common sense tells us that something is fundamentally wrong in rural America — economically, ecologically, and socially.

Common sense tells many farmers they would *not* be better off in some other occupation, even if they could make more money. Common sense also tells them they can't continue to take from nature without giving something back to nature, no matter what new technologies science may create. Common sense tells them that positive relationships with other people, with their families and communities, make their lives better, regardless of where they might choose to live.

Our common sense tells the rest of us that we must help farmers develop farming systems that can meet the needs of the present while leaving equal or better opportunities for the future. Our common sense also tells us that our food and farming systems must be ecologically sound, economically viable, and socially responsible if they are to be sustainable over time. And, our common sense tells us that an industrial, corporately controlled agriculture is not sustainable.

Our common sense also tells us that we can and must find ways to live and work that nurture the personal, interpersonal, and spiritual aspects of our lives. We know that we must accept responsibility for ourselves — that our individual well-being is important to our quality of life. But we know also, that caring for other people is not a sacrifice, but instead, our compassion and respect for others adds to the quality of our own life. And we know that taking care of the land is not a sacrifice, but instead stewardship of the earth helps give purpose and meaning to our lives. We know the quality of our life is enhanced when we make conscious, purposeful decisions to care for the earth and for each other. It's a matter of common sense.

We need not condemn ourselves for having failed to rely on our common sense. Even the founding fathers of our country sometimes denied their common sense in favor of conventional wisdom. The rightness of owning slaves was conventional wisdom until well into the 19th century — it had always been done. Until the 20th century, women in the U.S. were denied the right to vote — the conventional wisdom: their husbands should vote for them.

Conventional wisdom today says that farms must become still larger and fewer if farmers are to survive economically. Conventional wisdom says that agribusiness corporations can take better care of the land than can family farmers and that "free markets" will ensure that all are well-fed. Conventional wisdom says that family farms and rural communities are but nostalgic memories of a past that can never again become reality. But the conventional wisdom concerning American agriculture is wrong. It's time to reject the conventional wisdom. It's time to use our common sense.

2002

45 Is Capitalism Sustainable?

I realize most people who are interested in small farm issues are probably most interested in the practical aspects of farming and rural life. But, some of the really big questions confronting humanity are simply too important to leave to the economists and politicians. If our capitalistic economy is not sustainable, neither are our farms or ultimately our communities, our society or humanity. Some questions are so important that no one can afford to remain uninformed, uncommitted, and uninvolved.

Is capitalism sustainable? Not the type of capitalism that dominates American and most global economies today. This is not a matter of personal opinion, but a direct consequence of the most fundamental laws of science. Sustainability ultimately depends upon energy because anything that is useful in sustaining life on earth ultimately relies on energy. All material things that are of any use to humans — food, clothes, houses, automobiles, — require energy to make and energy to use. All useful human activities — working, thinking — require human energy. Physical scientists lump all such useful activities together and call them "work." All work requires energy.

In performing work, energy is always changed in form. In fact, the natural tendency of energy to change from more concentrated to less concentrated forms gives energy its ability to perform work. All material things, such as food, gasoline, plastic, and steel, are just highly concentrated forms of energy. Matter can be converted into energy, as in eating food or burning gasoline, and the form of energy can be changed, as in using heat to make electricity and electricity to produce light. However, even though work invariably changes matter to energy or changes the form of energy, no energy is lost. This is the first law of thermodynamics, the law of energy conservation, as in Einstein's famous $E=mc^2$.

At first, it might seem that energy could simply be recycled and reused forever, as if sustainability would be inevitable. However, once energy is used to perform work, before it can be used again, it must be reconcentrated, reorganized, and restored. Unfortunately, it takes energy to reconcentrate, reorganize, and restore energy. And, the energy used to reconcentrate and restore energy is simply no longer available to do anything else. It has lost its usefulness. This is the law of *entropy*, the second law of thermodynamics; the tendency of all closed systems to tend toward the ultimate degradation of matter and energy; toward inert uniformity; an absence of structure, pattern, organization, or differentiation. The barren surfaces of the Moon or Mars are examples of systems near entropy.

Since loss of useful energy to entropy is inevitable, it might seem that sustainability is impossible. Even if waste and pollution could be completely avoided in the processes of using and reusing energy, the tendency toward entropy would continue. In fact, life on earth would not be sustainable without the daily inflow of new solar energy. Sustainability ultimately depends upon the use of solar energy to offset the unavoidable effects of entropy.

Capitalism is a very efficient system of energy extraction, but it provides no incentive to reconcentrate and restore energy to offset entropy. Capitalists have no economic incentive to invest in energy renewal for the benefit of those of future generations. Capitalists reduce waste and pollution or reuse resources only when it is profitable to do so, meaning only when it is in their individual self-interest to do so. Capitalists have incentives to use renewable energy to support current consumption, but not to re-storing energy for future generations. Capitalism inevitably tends toward *physical entropy*.

The law of entropy applies to social energy as well as physical energy. All forms of human energy — labor, management, innovation, creativity — are products of social relationships. Humans cannot be born, reach maturity, and become *useful* without the help of other people who care about them *personally*. People must be educated, trained, civilized, and socialized before they can become productive members of complex societies. All organizations — including business organizations, governments, and economies — depend on the ability of people to work together for a common purpose, which in turn depend upon the sociability and civility of human societies. Human productivity is a direct result of healthy personal relationships, within families, friendships, communities, and societies.

Capitalism inevitably dissipates, disperses, and disorganizes social energy because it weakens personal relationships. Maximum economic efficiency requires that people relate to each other *impartially,* which means *impersonally.* People must compete rather than cooperate if market economies are to function efficiently. When people spend more time and energy working — being economically productive — they have less time and energy to spend on personal relationships within families and communities. When people buy things based solely on price rather than buy from people they know and trust, personal relationships within communities suffer from neglect. Capitalism devalues personal relationships and disconnects people and thus dissipates, disperses, and disorganizes social energy.

Capitalistic economies *use* people to do work, while doing nothing to restore the "social capital" needed to sustain positive personal relationships. There is no economic incentive for capitalists to invest in families, communities, or society for the benefit of future generations. Capitalists build relationships or contribute to social causes only when such contributions are expected to contribute to their profits or growth. Capitalists do not waste energy by investing in social capital. Capitalism inevitably tends toward *social entropy.*

Economies are simply the means by which people facilitate their relationships with other people and with their natural environment in complex societies. Economies actually *produce* nothing; they simply transform physical and social energy into raw materials and human labor, which can be exchanged in *impersonal* marketplaces. All economic capital is extracted from either natural or social capital. Once all natural and social capital has been extracted, there will be no source of economic capital. Without capital, an economy loses its ability to produce; it tends toward *economic entropy.* Today's capitalistic economies quite simply are not sustainable.

A sustainable economy must be based on a fundamentally different paradigm, specifically, on the paradigm of living systems. Living things by nature are self-making, self-renewing, reproductive, and regenerative. Living plants have the natural capacity to capture, organize, and store solar energy, both to support other living organisms and to offset the energy that is inevitably lost to entropy. Living things also have a natural propensity to reproduce their species. Humans, for example, devote large amounts of time and energy to raising families, with very little economic incentive to do so. Obviously, an individual life is not sustainable because every living thing eventually dies. But communities and societies of living individuals clearly have the capacity and natural propensity to be productive, while devoting a significant part of their life's energy to conceiving and nurturing the next generation.

Relationships within healthy living systems must be mutually beneficial, and thus must be *selective* in nature. All living organisms are made up of cells and each living cell is surrounded by a selective or semi-permeable membrane. These semi-permeable boundaries keep some things in but let other things out and keep some things out but let other things in. Living organisms likewise are defined by boundaries — skin, bark, scales — that selectively allow different elements — air, water, food, waste — to enter and to leave the body of the organism. If these boundaries were either completely permeable or impermeable, the organism would be incapable of life, and thus incapable of producing or reproducing.

The same principle holds for all living systems: ecosystems, families, communities, economies, cultures. The relationships among elements of healthy natural ecosystems are by nature mutually beneficial. However, relationships among humans and between humans and nature are matters of choice, and thus, must be consciously and purposefully selective. People must be willing and able to choose to maintain positive relationships with other people and to choose to take care of the earth, not only for their benefit but also to benefit those of future generations.

Capitalism provides no economic incentives to sustain life on earth, but humans have the innate capacity and natural tendency to do so. Throughout human history, people have chosen families, communities, and societies over isolation, even when it was not in their short-run, individual self-interests to do so. Throughout human history, people have shown a sense of respect and reverence toward the earth, and have attempted to care for the earth, even when there was no incentive to do so. It's only within the past few decades that humans in large numbers have abandoned their basic nature as caring, moral beings to pursue their narrow, individual self-interests. Not until the last few decades were the social and ethical constraints removed, turning capitalism into an unsustainable system of extraction and exploitation.

To restore sustainability, people must make conscious, purposeful decisions to rely on renewable energy, not just for consumption but also to rebuild stocks of natural capital for the benefit of future generations. To restore sustainability to capitalism, people must make conscious, purposeful choices to rebuild positive, mutually beneficial relationships with other people, not just for economic gains but also to restore depleted stocks of social capital. No other economic system even approaches the efficiency of capitalism in utilizing economic capital to meet individual material human needs and wants. But natural and social capital must be continually renewed and replenished to sustain economic capital. The sustainability of capitalism is simply too important to be left to the politicians and economists.

Is capitalism sustainable? This question ultimately must be addressed by all people, including those who operate small farms. You don't have to be a "rocket scientist" to understand the importance of energy, society, economics, and entropy to sustainability. All people have the ability and responsibility to understand the importance of questions of sustainability and to do whatever they can to address them. People on small farms are just as important in sustaining humanity as anyone else; they are not only real farmers but also real people.

2007

46 | Agroecology: The Science of Sustainable Agriculture

*A*groecology, as the name suggests, is an integration of agriculture and ecology. Agroecosystems are farms, agricultural systems, viewed from an ecological perspective. Agroecology is the science of design and management of *sustainable* agroecosystems, or more simply, *the science of sustainable agriculture.* The explicit purpose of integrating agriculture with ecology is to enhance the sustainability of agriculture.

Agroecology is not a commonly used word, even among advocates of sustainable agriculture. It has been around for more than twenty years, but somehow the concept has just never caught on, even among agricultural scientists. I suspect this is mostly because the advocates of agroecology have never explained why it is necessary to integrate agriculture with ecology in order to achieve agricultural sustainability. Maybe they thought it was obvious to all that agriculture must be viewed from an ecological perspective if it is to be sustainable. But it's not obvious to all, apparently even not to many agricultural scientists.

To understand the importance of agroecology, we have to return to its roots — to its first principles. First principles are different from values. Different people may have different values but first principles are true for everyone at all times. In earlier times, first principles referred to *natural law,* the nature of being human, as when our Founding Fathers declared, "We hold these truths to be self evident." First principles also refer to the *laws of nature,* meaning the principles that govern all natural physical phenomena. First principles cannot be proven, but they need no proof; they are "self-evident." In fact, all scientific principles are rooted in first principles, which were not and cannot be proven — they are accepted by science as self-evident.

The first principles of agroecology quite logically must be derived from the first principles of agriculture and ecology. Agriculture, by its basic nature, is a *purposeful* human activity. The basic purpose of agriculture is to shift the ecological balance of nature in favor of humans relative to other species. All species attempt to tip the balance in their favor; humans are no different in this regard. But, humans alone are a *willful* species. The rightness or legitimacy of agriculture is determined by its purpose, by *why* humans attempt to tip the ecological balance in their favor, and concurrently, *how far* they are willing to tip it.

The first principle of agriculture, and of agroecology, is *life has purpose.* If there is not purpose for life, there is no purpose for human life, and thus no purpose for agriculture — agriculture becomes a senseless activity. Most people probably never question whether life has purpose, but scientists do. Most scientists are philosophical *materialists,* at least in the practice of their professions. In his classic 1919 book, *Modern Science and Materialism,* Hugh Elliott, states, "The age of science is necessarily an age of materialism; ours is a scientific age, and it may be said with truth that we are all materialists now."

Elliott emphasized the primary assumptions of materialism. The first assumption asserts that when the conditions at any moment in time are precisely the same as those prevailing at some earlier moment, the results also will be identical to the earlier results. True causes and effects are always replicable. The second assumption of materialism is the denial of purpose. Elliott writes, "Scientific materialism . . . asserts that all events are due to the interaction of matter and motion, acting by blind necessity in accordance with those invariable sequences to which we have given the name laws." Human life is nothing more than an interaction of motion and matter. The third assumption of materialism denies the existence of spirituality — anything that lacks tangible, material characteristics and qualities. Among those things, he includes not only gods and souls, but also such entities as intellect, will, and feelings, insofar as they are supposed to be different from material processes.

Perhaps this is why agricultural scientists are so reluctant to address issues of sustainable agriculture; agricultural sciences deal only with the *processes* of agriculture, without questioning its *purpose,* or even admitting that it has one. They don't want to question the ethics or morality of today's industrial agriculture because the answers to such questions require intellect, willfulness, feelings, and ultimately, spirituality.

Thankfully, most ordinary people reject the philosophy of scientific materialists. Most people do not believe their choices and actions are predetermined acts of blind necessity or the inevitable consequences of ongoing interactions of matter and motion. They know they can't control their future, but they believe they can affect their future, through their willful choices. Ordinary people act as if their actions have meaning, believing their choices can be right or wrong and good or bad. Lacking purpose, right or wrong and good or bad are indistinguishable. Purpose in life may be rejected by science, but it is expressed in the social norms and customs of every civilized society and in the constitutions and laws of every credible government in the world. If human life has purpose, then agriculture too has purpose.

The first principle of ecology, and the second principle of agroecology, is that *all life is interconnected.* Deep ecologists go even farther in proclaiming the interconnectedness of not only biological communities but also all local and global communities — biological, human, non-human — in the past as well as in the present. While some ecologists might disagree about the relevance of connections among living things over time, ecologists agree that all of life is interconnected. While ordinary people may disagree about the relative importance of specific connections, their consensus seems to be in agreement with this second principle of agroecology.

The third principle of agroecology comes from both agriculture and ecology: *all life is good.* If all life is bad or evil, neither agriculture nor ecology makes sense. It would make no sense to be concerned with the health, vitality, or survival of living communities, species, or ecosystems if continuation of life on earth were not inherently good. Obviously, the death of individuals is an inevitable and natural aspect of life, but communities, species, and ecosystems are capable of renewal and regeneration and, thus are capable of sustaining and renewing themselves. While individuals, communities, and species may appear to pursue their self-interests, within their larger ecosystems, most individuals function naturally in ways that enhance the long-run sustainability of life. Nature, including both *laws of nature* and *natural law,* is biased in favor of life. This natural bias is enough to convince many people that life is good.

Many other logical, reasonable, thoughtful people simply reject the assumptions of scientific materialism. They believe that people have free will, that life has purpose, and life is spiritual — that intellect, will, and feelings are more than material processes. They believe in an intangible, unknowable higher order of things, within which all aspects of reality, including all life, have purpose and meaning. And they believe that life was meant to be good. Very few people believe that reality and life are inherently evil, and those who do are generally labeled as sociopaths. It doesn't matter whether the principle of goodness arises from the natural bias or nature of the goodness of some higher order; both arise as matters of faith. Such is the nature of first principles; they cannot be proven, but require no proof. They exist because people know they exist. Without first principles, life simply makes no sense.

The question of the rightness or goodness of any particular kind of agriculture, then, can be derived from the first principles of agroecology. Since human life is interconnected with all other life, an agriculture that is good for all life, including life across all generations, is good. An agriculture that diminishes life, including the quality of human life, is bad. An agriculture that enhances life is right, and an agriculture that diminishes life is wrong. Aldo Leopold expressed much the same conclusion in his classic essay, *The Land Ethic,* when he wrote, "A thing is right when it tends to preserve the integrity, stability, and beauty of the biotic community. It is wrong when it tends otherwise." His *land ethic* asked us to "examine each question in terms of what is ethically and esthetically right, as well as what is economically expedient." Any science of sustainable agriculture must be rooted in such an ethic — in the first principles of agroecology.

I have been criticized by my academic colleagues over the years because I am obviously an advocate for sustainable agriculture and an opponent of industrial agriculture. They argue that science must be objective, meaning scientists should make no judgment regarding what kind of agriculture is good or bad or right or wrong. But all science is rooted in such judgments, regardless of whether they are admitted or even recognized by scientists. The current science supporting large-scale, industrial agriculture is rooted in the assumption that productivity and profits will serve the long-run needs of humanity, regardless of the short-run ecological and social consequences. I fail to find any logical or reasonable set of first principles that will support such an assumption.

My opposition to industrial agriculture is rooted in the fact that it diminishes life — life in the soil, life in fields and feedlots, life in rural communities, and life of consumers who eat industrial foods. My advocacy of sustainable, small farm agriculture is based on the first principles of agroecology, the science of sustainability: life has purpose, all life is connected, and life is good. I believe that life on a small farm can be a good life and that's what *real* farming is about.

2007

End Notes

Chapter 1. First presented at the 2nd National Small Farm Conference, St. Louis, MO, October 12–15, 1999, organized by the USDA CSREES Small Farms Program and Lincoln University.

Chapter 2. First appeared in *Small Farm Today,* September–October 2000.

Chapter 3. First appeared in *Small Farm Today,* March–April 2001.

Chapter 4. First appeared in *Small Farm Today,* November–December 2002.

Chapter 5. First appeared in *Small Farm Today,* January–February 2005.

Chapter 6. First appeared in *Small Farm Today,* March–April 2006.

Chapter 7. First appeared in *Small Farm Today,* May–June 2001.

Chapter 8. First appeared in *Small Farm Today,* July–August 2000.

Chapter 9. First appeared in *Small Farm Today,* November–December 2001.

Chapter 10. First appeared in *Small Farm Today,* September–October 2003.

Chapter 11. First appeared in *Small Farm Today,* July–October 2006.

Chapter 12. First appeared in *Missouri Farm,* February 1993.

Chapter 13. First appeared in *Missouri Farm,* May–June 1991.

Chapter 14. First appeared in *Small Farm Today,* May–June 2001.

Chapter 15. First appeared in *Small Farm Today,* January–February 2003.

Chapter 16. First appeared in *Small Farm Today,* July–August 2004.

Chapter 17. First appeared in *Small Farm Today,* September–October 2005.

Chapter 18. First appeared in *Small Farm Today,* February 1994.

Chapter 19. First appeared in *Small Farm Today,* November–December 2000.

Chapter 20. First appeared in *Small Farm Today,* July–August 2003.

Chapter 21. First appeared in *Small Farm Today,* September–October 2004.

Chapter 22. First appeared in *Small Farm Today,* May–June 2006.

Chapter 23. First appeared in *Small Farm Today,* May–June 2002.

Chapter 24. First appeared in *Small Farm Today,* September–October 2001.

Chapter 25. First appeared in *Small Farm Today,* March–April 2003.

Chapter 26. First appeared in *Small Farm Today,* January–February 2004.

Chapter 27. First appeared in *Small Farm Today,* May–June 2004.

Chapter 28. First appeared in *Small Farm Today,* May–June 2003.

Chapter 29. First appeared in *Small Farm Today,* May–June 2005.

Chapter 30. First appeared in *Small Farm Today,* March–April 2005.

Chapter 31. First appeared in *Small Farm Today,* July–August 2005.

Chapter 32. First appeared in *Small Farm Today*, July–August 2007.

Chapter 33. First appeared in *Sustainable Alternative Farming Institute Newsletter*, Winter 2001.

Chapter 34. First appeared in *Small Farm Today*, July–August 2001.

Chapter 35. First appeared in *Small Farm Today*, November–December 2003.

Chapter 36. First appeared in *Small Farm Today*, November–December 2005.

Chapter 37. First appeared in *Small Farm Today*, March–April 2006.

Chapter 38. First appeared in *Small Farm Today*, January–February 2002.

Chapter 39. First appeared in *Small Farm Today*, March–April 2002.

Chapter 40. First appeared in *Small Farm Today*, September–October 2002.

Chapter 41. First appeared in *Small Farm Today*, March–April 2004.

Chapter 42. First appeared in *Small Farm Today*, January–February 2001.

Chapter 43. First appeared in *Small Farm Today*, November–December 2004.

Chapter 44. First appeared in *Small Farm Today*, July–August 2002.

Chapter 45. First appeared in *Small Farm Today*, May–June 2007.

Chapter 46. First appeared in *Small Farm Today*, March–April 2007.

Index

Conservation Reserve Program, 55
Conservation Security Act, 130
contract production, 104
conventional, 66
conventional wisdom, 230-231
cooperatives, 21, 154-155
corporate welfare, 128
corporations, 12, 174-175
costs, 52-53
costs, ecological, 179
costs, transportation, 163
Covey, Stephen, 155-156
crisis, 2
crisis, food, 176
cross-fertilized, 225
cultural creatives, 150
Cultural Creatives, The, 149-150

Daly, Herman, 122-123
DDT, 194
deep ecologists, 239
depression, mental, 134-135
Descartes, Rene, 204
diabetes, 193
dime, 14-15
diversified, 201
diversity, 68

eat local, statistics, 162
eat local, top ten list, 163-166
eating, 148
ecological benefits, 109
ecological costs, 109
ecologically sound, 6
economic benefit, 108
economic costs, 108
economic equity, 129
economically viable, 6
economics, 122, 123

economy, ecological, 124
economy, free market, 125
economy, private, 123
economy, social, 123-124
ecosystem, 192
Elliott, Hugh, 238
employment security, 128, 129, 130
energy conservation, 233
energy, 69
energy, fossil, 188-189
energy, nuclear, 220
energy, renewable, 188
energy, solar, 233, 234
energy, wind, 189-190
entropy, 89, 209-210, 211, 233
entropy, economical, 234
entropy, physical, 233
entropy, social, 234
ethics, 142
eudaimonia, 133-134
evolution, 139, 117
exploitation, 111-112, 144
extensive, 9

farm and agribusiness, 41-42
farm management, 106
farm programs, 127
farms, commercial, 54, 55
farms, stewardship, 54-55, 216
Fast Food Nation, 181
fast food, 181
fences, 208
food costs, 96
food quality, 163
food security, 167-168
food, convenient, 180
food, quick, 180-181
For the Common Good, 122-123